His mouth ta
warm and in

'Happy New Yea...
as the clock struck midnight.

Gina Tarantino looked up into the grey-blue eyes
of the tall man who'd just kissed her and felt a
tangible jolt of pure hunger. Gina blinked as she
stared at Jackson Gray and tried to find her
equilibrium.

He looked rough. His dark hair was brushed back
from a face full of secrets. His black sweater and
black jeans didn't offer a clue to his personality.
He was a stranger.

'Let's get out of here,' Jackson whispered.

What harm could it do to be kissed again? To be
held? To take one night for herself?

Gina looked into his eyes, into the radiant
sexiness of the smile curving his mouth, and took
the first leap into a new life. 'Lead the way.'

Dear Reader,

New Year's Eve is a very special time for me. Somehow, in that one evening, all the memories of the past are brought together with our hopes for the future. It is a time of new beginnings. What better setting could I ask for my contribution to the IT HAPPENED ONE NIGHT mini-series, *New Year's Knight*?

Officer Gina Tarantino closes her own chapter on the past by righting an old wrong on New Year's Eve. Then, she unexpectedly finds her own new beginning in the arms of a sexy stranger. Their night of love becomes a source of healing for both of them.

From the moment bad boy Jackson Gray came on the scene in my December Temptation®, *Christmas Knight*, I knew I'd created a character I wouldn't soon forget. He hides behind a 'tough guy' exterior and only Gina can recognize the vulnerable man underneath. He's a man after my own heart, who deserves his own story. I hope you feel the same.

Wishing you a year filled with new beginnings,

Lyn Ellis

NEW YEAR'S KNIGHT

BY

LYN ELLIS

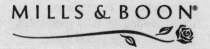

MILLS & BOON®

*MILLS & BOON and MILLS & BOON with the Rose Device
are registered trademarks of the publisher.
TEMPTATION is a registered trademark of
Harlequin Enterprises Limited, used under licence.*

*First published in Great Britain 1998
by Harlequin Mills & Boon Limited,
Eton House, 18-24 Paradise Road, Richmond, Surrey TW9 1SR*

© Gin Ellis 1997

ISBN 0 263 80790 8

To:
Vince D.—cyber studmuffin. Thanks for the 'dad' stuff,
and a few other things.
And to Sandra, my fairy godmother,
for the white picket fence.

21-9801

*Printed and bound in Great Britain
by Caledonian International Book Manufacturing Ltd, Glasgow*

1

HIS MOUTH TASTED like champagne—warm and intoxicating.

"Happy New Year," he murmured, close to her lips as the clock struck midnight.

Officer Gina Tarantino looked up into the gray-blue eyes of the tall man who'd just kissed her and felt a tangible jolt of pure hunger. She shivered.

How long had it been since she'd been kissed...really kissed by a man who wanted her? Too long. A wave of dizziness swam over her. Gina blinked as she stared at Jackson Gray, and tried to find her equilibrium.

He looked rough. A man with edges who would never offer pretty words. His dark blond hair was brushed back from a face full of secrets. The black sweater and black jeans he wore didn't offer a clue to his identity except that the sweater felt soft and expensive, and the jeans fit as if they'd been made expressly for him. He could be anything from a construction worker to a rock star.

And he was a *stranger*. She'd just kissed a stranger and the physical connection between them still sizzled inside her like a downed power wire dancing in a rain-storm.

Get ahold of yourself! her logic ordered. *You weren't even invited to this party. You've delivered the message and righted an old wrong. Now wish him Happy New Year and get the hell out of here.*

"Dance with me," Jackson said. His large hand moved to her arm and she allowed him to pull her forward without protest. As he drew her close to his chest, she breathed in the clean, male scent of him, and the dizziness returned.

Gina twisted her fingers into the warm softness of Jackson's sweater to hold on, to him and to her balance. He guided her steps with firm ease, using his substantial body... and his hands. The slow teasing touch of his chest to her breasts, his breath in her hair, nearly made her faint.

She sighed and relaxed against him. *Happy New Year*, she said to herself. And at that moment, she felt radiantly alive, and as new as the year. With each movement of Jackson's body in time with hers, Gina's heavy weight of responsibilities—the husband she'd lost, the child he'd given her—seemed to evaporate. Tomorrow she'd still be Gina, but tonight she could be a stranger too.

She wanted to drink more champagne, to laugh and pretend that her heart had never been broken. To pretend that she'd been invited to the ball and that the stroke of midnight didn't mean an ending, but a beginning. She could dance forever if she wanted.

And, she wanted to dance with this man. To be surrounded by him and the reckless feelings ricocheting around inside her. He wasn't forever, but for tonight, he was a temptation she didn't want to resist.

Stretching against Jackson's chest, she brought her arms upward and looped them around his neck. He was so tall, her fingers barely brushed the long hair at his collar. He shifted to accommodate the change but looked down to meet her eyes.

So intense. An uncommon urge to giggle rose inside Gina. The twinkling lights of the party seemed to spin around her. She wanted to see him smile, to watch his harsh features relax, to laugh with him because it was New Year's and because they were strangers and . . . because there was magic in the air.

That's when she decided to kiss him again. At first, it was teasing and playful but when she started to pull away, he wouldn't let her go. He followed her without breaking the contact of their mouths and deepened the kiss, taking control, coaxing her mouth open with the brush of his tongue.

"Let's get out of here," Jackson said after kissing her thoroughly. He shifted Gina close to his side as if she belonged there, and they walked past the other dancing couples toward the entrance of the Nova Gallery where the New Year's Eve celebration was being held.

Gina felt like a sleepwalker although she was more alert than she'd been in years. It didn't occur to her to be afraid or hesitant. She felt good and wanted more of the same. What harm could it do to be kissed again? To be held? What harm could it do to take something, one night, for herself?

She allowed Jackson to guide her into the courtyard. The cold night air swirled around her, and she shivered. She'd left her jacket in her car.

"Are you cold?" Jackson asked. Not waiting for an answer, he enfolded her into his arms and lowered his mouth to hers.

No, she wasn't cold any longer. He delved into her mouth as if he couldn't get close enough or deep enough and she opened to him. His hands ran upward from her waist, then his fingers dug into the muscles of her back causing her to arch against him. She moaned and the sound of her own pleasure shocked her. It had been so long . . .

Jackson dragged his mouth away from hers. "Easy," he whispered raggedly. He held them perfectly still for a few labored breaths then he moved as if he'd made a decision. "Come on." He took her hand and tugged her forward.

"Where are we going?" she managed to ask.

"My place," he said without looking at her. He cut straight across the grass of the courtyard toward a door at the far end. He stopped in front of it and turned to face her. For the first time, he looked hesitant. "Do you want to come inside?" he asked, as if he'd suddenly remembered she was a cop. Or as if he knew they were flying faster than the speed of light.

Gina knew what he was asking. Did she want to go inside, into the warm darkness with this man? Yes. Right then she wanted anything Jackson was willing to give. But the cop in her, the responsible, careful, sensible part of her knew she needed to slow down and think.

The reckless, reawakened woman inside her uniform however, wasn't listening. Who would she be hurting? She was a widow. Her daughter was spending the night with a playmate. All her friends had someone tonight. And Gina was beginning another year alone.

Like a flash from the past, Gina could almost hear her protective older brother's voice. *Wadda you? Nuts? For all you know he could be an ax murderer.* She almost smiled. To her brother Vince, every man who'd ever asked her out had been a potential maniac. She was old enough now to take care of herself.

"How do you feel about condoms?" she asked.

Jackson's smile was dazzling, even in the dark. Gina felt her heart start to beat in slow heavy thuds. He was beautiful when he smiled. Well, not exactly beautiful but . . . He ran long blunt fingers upward along the inside of her arm and tugged her a little closer. "I never leave home without 'em," he quipped. "And since we *are* home . . ." He opened the door and waited.

Gina looked into his eyes, into the radiant sexiness of the smile curving his mouth and took the first leap into a new life.

The dim glow of blue neon bent into the shape of Japanese calligraphy lit one corner of the room giving enough light to vaguely make out the shapes of comfortable-looking furniture. Jackson guided her in another direction, however.

The silence in the building should have made her uneasy, but his warm hand was curled around hers and the taste of him was still on her lips. They passed an oversize door on the left which was open. Inside sat a huge chrome-and-black motorcycle. Gina recognized the wings on the insignia. Harley-Davidson. A black leather jacket had been tossed across the seat.

Her mind was slowly computing the image. Motorcycle equals biker. But then he stopped in the hallway to kiss her again and she folded into him as he wrapped his arms around her and lifted her from the ground, kissing her the entire time. She pushed away the nagging voice of caution.

Jackson was so big and silent. Completely vulnerable, Gina should have been afraid. Yet, she wasn't. She felt totally safe and unable to deny herself what she was longing for. Jackson was solid and warm and real. She wanted this night and this man.

He backed into the bedroom holding her and tightened his grip before falling backward onto a huge bed. His arms relaxed, and Gina found herself sprawled on his broad chest. The tables had turned. Now he was the vulnerable one. The lower part of his body shifted and she heard a boot hit the floor. He moved again and the other one landed next to the first. Gina kicked off her own shoes then squirmed against him like a cat searching for the softest place on a pillow, or in this case the hardest.

With a low laugh, Jackson brought his hands to rest on her hips. "You comfortable up there?"

Gina smiled into the darkness, found his jaw with her fingers, and told the truth. "Yeah. I think I like being on top."

He answered her by moving his legs and pressing her hips downward, into the rock hard evidence straining against his jeans. "I like it, too. Come on, show me what you want."

Gina sucked in a breath as he slowly rocked upward against her. Her body seemed to ignite from the contact and she moved with him, echoing from the center out. Before she could think, her fingers delved into his hair and she tugged his head upward to meet her kiss. She shifted her legs to straddle his hips, and he moaned into her mouth.

Dizziness struck again, Gina felt drunk with her own long-denied passion, and power. She was used to taking control in her job, and in her home life as a single mom. But this kind of opportunity, of having a tempting man in the darkness without questions or guilt—or expectations—made her feel as if she'd downed a whole bottle of champagne instead of a few glasses.

Gina didn't intend to question it. With new determination, she pushed backward, away from his kiss, away from the warm tongue teasing her own, and sat up.

Insinuating her hands under the bottom edge of his sweater, she shoved it upward. It needed to come off—now. She lost her intent, however, when her palms came in contact with his warm, flat belly and then his chest. She forgot the sweater and leaned forward again to kiss the pliant skin and hard muscle with its sprinkling of soft hair.

He curled upward. His arms flexed and suddenly the sweater was gone, out of her way. Then his fingers drew her shirt from the security of her belt, and began working the buttons.

Reality whirled away. Gina knew she'd stepped onto the roller coaster. The door to the past closed behind her and locked. This man, who *wasn't* Mike, was about to rock her world. She gasped as his hands pushed under her bra and cupped her breasts. The breathless ride picked up speed.

She arched her back offering her breasts to his hands and he groaned like a man in pain before he bracketed her rib cage and dragged her to meet his mouth.

Gina could barely breathe. She went perfectly still in his hands, as he drew on her nipples, transforming them into diamond hard points of pleasure. He laved her with his tongue then sucked harder before grazing one throbbing nipple with his teeth. Her whole body seemed to clench and she couldn't stop the low answering moan that rose inside her. Jackson briefly broke contact with his mouth and shoved at her belt.

"Help me . . . Get these off," he directed before returning to her breasts.

Gina wanted to help, but each time she tried to get her belt undone, he rewarded her with a more lavish sensual attack. In very short order, she lost the ability to think all together. "Come on, honey. Get out of those pants. I promise, you'll feel a lot better soon."

After several tries, she managed to get her belt unfastened and the zipper down. He followed her movements with his mouth, keeping contact as if to encourage her to get the job done quicker. Finally he helped her shove the slacks down her legs.

He slid his hands, palms flat, down the length of her naked back from shoulders to thighs and the smooth friction sent a quiver of pleasure through her.

He went very still beneath her. "Are you all right?" he asked, concerned.

"Are you kidding?" Her own breathless laugh sounded foreign to her. She wasn't afraid, and she didn't want him to stop. They'd stepped into the tornado, and now she wanted to fly.

"Hold on, then." With one smooth movement, Jackson rolled them over until she was underneath him. He balanced on his elbows easing most of his upper body weight off her and ran his fingers along her cheek to her lips. She retaliated by opening her mouth to his touch and catching one finger between her teeth. He kissed her, replacing his fingers with his tongue.

"Let me turn on a light in here," he said, breaking away from her mouth. "I want to see you...." He reached toward the table at the edge of the bed.

"No." The urgency in her voice and her hands as she held him back stopped him. "Please. I want ..." She *didn't* want to spoil the magic with explanations or reality. "I'm not afraid of the dark," she whispered. *Because in the dark I can be a stranger. . . .*

On this night, she wanted to be his. She arched and drew him downward, her hands at his waist, nudging him, reminding him that he was still half dressed. At her insistence, he seemed to forget about the light and slowly rose to his knees to unfasten his pants. There was enough light to see the strong line of his broad shoulders tapering to his waist. To watch him push the material of his jeans down and kick them off.

Then he stopped to stare down at her. Gina's heart was pounding so hard she could almost hear the blood rushing through her veins. Excitement and fear, newness and familiarity, recklessness and need all tumbled through her senses. Ready or not . . .

But instead of covering her again, he bent and ran his tongue along one of her thighs then nuzzled the soft hair he found at the end of the journey. Goose bumps rose on her skin as he drew in a deep breath, as if he wanted to smell her. . . taste her. He slowly guided her legs apart and Gina felt her thigh muscles quake under his hands. Then his tongue touched the center of her and she was lost.

Pleasure rippled through her as he used his tongue until she was gasping and twisting beneath him. Until she was so close to the edge of what they both wanted that she couldn't have stopped him.

As if he knew what she was feeling, Jackson paused and stretched away from her. All she could think of was bringing him back. She didn't want him to leave her now. Not now! But he resisted.

"It's okay," he said sounding out of breath. "Just a second..."

Gina realized what he was doing when she opened her eyes and saw him poised over her. Getting the condom. He'd remembered. If she hadn't been so wild to have him she would have smiled.

She didn't have time though, because he was urging her legs farther apart and she tried to help him, encouraging him to hurry. But before she could reach out, he pushed inside her, and the hard feel of him, the slow, controlled strength of his movements sent the first scintillating convulsion through her. She arched her back, dug her fingers into his skin and held on.

"You feel...so...good." Jackson's low voice tickled her ear. He sounded breathless and shaken. And his obvious pleasure melted something inside Gina, robbing her of any semblance of control.

In four strokes she began to come apart like a house in a storm, gasping and crying out as she twisted and trembled and spun. In pleasure, not pain. In awe. She'd never experienced anything like the bone deep pleasure that was literally curling her toes. Not even with Mike.

She felt Jackson's arms tremble and tighten as he increased the rhythm that had become as powerful and important as her own heartbeat. She urged him with her hands, her pleasure still running warm through her blood.

"Come on," she whispered close to his ear. She wanted him to feel what she'd felt, to have part of what he'd given her. She used his words. "Come on, honey."

She felt him give in, reluctantly, as if he would by sheer will make the feeling last forever. With a wild sound that seemed to be caught in his chest, he shuddered and drove deeper into her. Then his big body seemed to relax all at once and his weight pressed her into the mattress.

It felt good. His heavy, warm limbs pinned her down. His chest rose and fell in deep replenishing breaths. She ran one hand through the damp hair at Jackson's neck and sighed. Well, she'd finally done it. She'd *been* with another man besides Mike. Of all the ways and times she'd imagined how this situation would occur, she'd never imagined anyone like Jackson Gray. She hadn't thought she'd respond to another man more than she'd responded to Mike. But she had and she couldn't change that fact. *Sorry, Mike,* she thought.

She didn't realize she'd said it aloud until the man in her arms stirred and asked, "Who's Mike?"

2

GINA SWALLOWED, easing the sudden tightness in her throat. "My husband," she whispered.

Every muscle in Jackson's body went from relaxed to taut. He raised himself onto one elbow and looked into her eyes. "You're married?"

The ominous tone in his voice sent a short burst of fear through Gina. In those few aching seconds she realized the precariousness of her situation. *Wadda you? Nuts?*

"No—not now," she answered quickly. Gina shut out the frightening image of what this man might look like angry and searched around inside for her own intuitive reading of the situation. *I'm a widow.* The words rose inside her but she couldn't say them, not when she was lying naked in another man's bed, when she'd just— Damn. She didn't feel the need to discuss her past now, or maybe ever, with this man...with...Jackson, but she wasn't afraid of him. She checked twice—no fear. As puzzling as it appeared, she felt safe.

He relaxed slightly and brushed the hair back from her face. "Good," he said. "I don't— I usually find out things like that before I—" A breath of relief warmed the skin along her cheek. "Good," he said again and kissed her lips lightly before sliding his weight off her. Before she could contemplate a graceful escape, he circled her in his arms and brought her against his side with her cheek resting on his shoulder.

"Gina." He said her name into the darkness, testing it like he would a foreign language. She didn't feel the need to answer, though she did have the urge to touch him again. She tentatively rested her palm flat against the center of his chest—so solid and warm.

"Gina..." It was a whisper this time, closer to her ear. He was pulling at her with the sound of her own name, coaxing her. She turned her head slightly and his lips were there, teasing and tempting her. He rose up, balanced on one arm and drew her to him as he kissed her, deeply and slowly. It was then that Gina realized that he didn't have to hold her down. All he needed to do was kiss her or touch her to make her want to get closer, to wrap herself around him like a bright silken scarf pushed by a warm summer breeze.

When the kiss ended, Gina drew in some much needed air and tried to recover her original plan—to make a graceful escape. "I really should go...." she said, trying to find the enthusiasm to take her hands off him.

"Don't..." he whispered. The vibration of his low voice and the need transmitted in that one word warmed her skin like a caress. One persuasive hand ran down her back to punctuate the promise. *More...to come.*

Gina shivered and moved closer. It didn't matter that she knew he was only temporary, someone she'd never have invited into her life. Right now, he was lying next to her, warm and steady, and oh so tempting. And she'd been sleeping alone for far too long.

Instead of stumbling over words she didn't have, she insinuated herself closer until her breasts brushed against his ribs before she slid one arm around his neck to bring his mouth back into range. It didn't take him long to realize he'd persuaded her.

JACKSON OPENED his eyes then squinted into the wedge of bright morning light blasting through the skylight in the ceiling. He didn't move or turn his head. He closed his eyes again for a moment, savoring the feel of the warm, feminine body sprawled against his side. The body of a woman who'd caused him to break most of his rules about who he brought to his bed.

The woman who'd kept him up most of the night.

The hot memory of the evening before opened his eyes and caused parts of his body to grow warm and taut. He turned to look at her.

Sleepyhead. Her face was turned away from him and her dark, nearly black hair spilled across the pillow. Finally, he could get a good daylight view of her fea-

tures, the angle of her cheekbone, the straight feminine profile of her nose. Her skin had the darker, golden
color that went with her midnight hair.

He wished she would open her eyes and look at him
again so he could see the exact color. So he could have
one more helping of the way she'd gazed at him right
before she'd kissed him at the party the night before.

Jackson felt himself harden once more as the fresh
memory played through his mind like a loop of video-
tape. When he'd tasted her shy initiation of the kiss, an
unprecedented shock of embarrassment had hit him.
He hadn't been set off like that since he was a teenager.
He'd tried to ease his lower body away from her, but
she'd clung to him like a woman standing on a ledge.
Even though he'd never been accused of being a gentleman, he wasn't about to let her fall.

They'd left the dance floor, but the look on her face
after the kiss had been etched into his mind like acid on
metal. She'd looked stunned. Her lips parted slightly
in invitation . . .

Now her eyes were closed and one of her hands rested
palm up on the pillow next to her face. She was sound
asleep like an exhausted child.

He slipped one of his hands under the sheet along her
stomach and nuzzled his face into her hair. She felt so
small and delicate and . . . smooth. She smelled like

shampoo and... *Gina*. He didn't say it out loud, didn't really want to wake her yet. He just needed to touch her.

When he kissed her ear, she shifted and sighed, stretching her back and unconsciously pushing her hips in his direction. Her unguarded response rippled up his spine like a shot of adrenaline. His skin grew warm from neck to groin. He couldn't resist pressing the hottest part of his anatomy against the cooler smoothness of her backside. His hand slipped lower, from her belly to the V of her thighs and she shifted her legs, opening to the contact.

Damn. Even asleep she turned him on. And he barely knew her. Jackson didn't know if he should be a gentleman and wake her up or do what his body was screaming for and talk about it later.

His fingers slipped into her warm wetness and she made a low murmur of pleasure. It made his jaw tighten with answering need and a coil of pure, unexpected possessiveness tightened inside him. He wanted to mark her as his own, with his mouth, his hands, his sex.

Just when he thought he wouldn't be able to resist plunging inside her, Gina turned in his arms and pushed her face into the space between his shoulder and neck. One of her hands slid along his ribs to his hip and she tugged him closer.

He thought of condoms and the distance between Gina's sleepy welcoming body and the top drawer on the far side of the bed. But before he could make his body release the woman it wanted and move to the drawer, Gina squirmed against his aching erection and dug her fingernails into the skin of his back.

He'd be careful, he told himself. He'd pull out and get a condom before anything momentous took place. But right now he just wanted to slide into her once, bare, with nothing artificial between them. To be completely surrounded and held by her smooth wet heat.

His body shifted and fulfilled his wish. What had seemed like a pleasant dream became reality. He groaned with the pleasure of the first stroke. A quake of aching satisfaction ran under his skin as she tightened around him. Gina drew in a long breath and anchored one arm around his back to hold him close. He didn't know whether she was awake or still dreaming. She kissed his neck and murmured something he couldn't decipher.

Jackson eased her over onto her back and began a slow rhythm that her body answered thrust for thrust. With each push he felt his body building toward climax. He'd stop in just a moment, in just a . . . Gina seemed to be waking up. Her limbs suddenly lost their lethargy and her legs shifted to wrap around his thighs as her arms tightened to hold him closer.

Then she was moaning, lost in her own pleasure beneath him. Nearing her own climax with a sweet, breathless hunger that matched his own. He tried to pull away. He pushed up onto his elbows in order to get out before he did something irrevocable. But she urgently dragged him back with a ragged groan and a look of unabashed pleasure on her flushed face. He'd underestimated the strength of her welcoming body lost in orgasm. The first convulsion of his own climax slammed through him before he managed to twist away and withdraw. Then, safely on the outside, he ground his hips against her as he was overtaken by his pleasure.

"Good morning," he whispered into her ear when his breathing had returned to normal.

"Mmm," she murmured, making no attempt to move.

Jackson felt an unfamiliar jolt of pleasure. At that moment he couldn't think of any other place he'd rather be than in his own bed with this woman, hearing the sound of her satisfaction. *Happy New Year.* He moved, so he could look into her eyes.

She smiled sleepily, and ran her fingers along his biceps. She started to say something but she stopped suddenly. The expression on her face changed drastically. She removed her hand from his arm and insinuated it between their stomachs, into the warm and wet evidence of his climax.

"The condom broke." She looked alarmed.

"No— I uh— I was going to get one but—" For the second time in twenty-four hours, Jackson felt tongue-tied. This time however, he wasn't enjoying the sensation. He wanted to say, *This doesn't usually happen to me.* To tell her that he never broke the rule about unprotected sex. He *knew* better. But, in her case he'd broken all his rules and he didn't know how to explain it. "Don't worry. I pulled out before—"

"Don't worry?" She looked like she wanted to dial 911. Instead she shoved at his chest. "Get off me!" she ordered in a panicked tone that couldn't be ignored.

He rolled away and with a whoosh, received the business end of a well-swung pillow right in his face.

"I trusted you!"

Jackson batted the pillow away and saw the pale flash of her bare limbs as she bent to pick up her clothes from the floor near the bed.

"Gina—"

A scathing look stopped his explanation. She faced him with her clothes in her arms and Jackson watched her panic shift to righteous anger. "I can't believe I trusted someone like you," she said. "Where's the shower?"

"Behind the glass block wall." Jackson watched her stalk away and tried to think of a way to apologize. He ended up wrapped in a sheet standing on the outside of the locked bathroom door. "I meant you don't have to worry—I don't have any diseases. I swear."

A long silence ensued.

"Gina?" Jackson felt like breaking the lock on the door but that might really scare her. She was already scared enough. He heard the shower come on and the sound of the glass doors being shut and knew she wasn't listening to him anymore.

GINA STOOD UNDER the hot, pounding water and tried to get her heart to stop racing. He'd said he didn't have any diseases . . . but how was he so sure? She knew better than to have casual sex. Nowadays it was too dangerous. Just the thought terrified her, and dredged up a wellspring of guilt. Emma only had her mother. If something happened, Gina knew her family would care for her daughter, but Emma would still be an orphan. Then another possibility occurred to her. What if she ended up presenting Emma with a little brother or sister?

Stop! the calmer part of her mind ordered. *Don't panic. You'll be fine.*

How could she have been such a nitwit? Thinking she could have an evening for herself without paying the consequences. Trusting a man whom she'd met once—nine hours ago. A man who looked capable of anything. For all she knew he could be wanted!

Oh, wouldn't that be a great story if it got around the station house? To the men she knew, she was either Emma's mom, a fellow police officer or Mike's wife, even though Mike had been dead for three years. To the policemen around her she'd always belong to him, as if she'd died that same night.

Yeah, did you hear about Mike's wife boinking that biker? Merely the thought of the relentless comments the guys on her shift would make gave her a headache.

Her New Year's resolution had been to start over. To put together a new life for Emma and herself. She wanted to find a normal, nice guy to make her family whole again. She wanted the white picket fence and all the trimmings; something even Mike hadn't been able to give her.

Mike's disapproving image floated in her mind. The guilt welling inside her deepened. She'd loved him, wished desperately she could have helped him. She didn't believe all those things he'd confessed on tape. But one fact was inescapable, she couldn't help him now—and he couldn't help her. The vows had been until death do us part.

You're the one who left, she thought, letting her anger surface. *If I decided to get involved with a biker, it was my choice.* Jackson had been her choice. She couldn't blame that on Mike or anyone else. *What a nitwit!*

She snatched a bar of soap from the shelf and started to scrub her skin. In the process, she began to take in her surroundings. Jackson didn't live like a biker. The bathroom was clean and well designed. Most of the walls were made of glass block and over her head she could see blue sky through a skylight. She wondered who had originally lived in the apartment. It had to have been someone with money.

Gina finished her shower and got dressed in her somewhat wrinkled police uniform. She used his toothpaste and her finger to scrub her teeth. She and Jackson had already shared more than a toothbrush but there was no sense pressing her luck. She couldn't find the clip for her hair, however, so she used his comb and left it at that. Then her mind returned to her fears.

She found him in the kitchen standing at the coffee maker, shirtless and shoeless, wearing only a pair of worn, blue jeans.

"How do you know you don't have any diseases?" she blurted out after barely stepping into the room. She didn't trust being alone with him anymore, or trust herself for that matter. Look what had happened because he'd kissed her on New Year's Eve.

He turned to face her, cocked one hip to lean against the counter and crossed his arms. In those few seconds Gina was doubly aware of how big he was. What did she know about him? A flashing instant replay of some of the more interesting moments from the night before skittered through her thoughts. She had to amend the question. She knew a few…physical things about him. She knew how gentle his big hands could be, how his mouth— To her utter disbelief she felt a blush rising up her neck.

"I give blood," he said, matter-of-factly. "I have a rare type and I go as often as they need me."

The building terror gripping Gina's stomach relaxed slightly.

"When was the last—"

"Three weeks ago," he answered, then pushed away from the counter and walked toward her. He ended up a few feet away with most of the kitchen table between them. "And I stopped taking chances years ago."

Gina felt like squirming. She spied her hair clip on the table and stepped closer to retrieve it. "Well, that's a relief," she said honestly. "Now I only have to worry about unplanned pregnancy." She shoved the hair clip in her pocket but before she could pull her hand free he had bracketed her shoulders with his hands.

"You don't take birth control?" He looked bigger and fiercer than he had only a few moments before and she didn't get it. Did he have some fear of being forced into a shotgun wedding? As if she'd want to marry him . . .

"It hasn't been necessary."

He closed his eyes and put his head back. Then he released her shoulders and rubbed his own neck as if it hurt. "Great." He sighed. He opened his eyes and looked at her again. "I know . . . I didn't ask."

Gina felt a little pained herself. "No, you didn't," she replied defensively. "And you said you'd use a condom."

"I did, every time—" he held her gaze "—except the last." He released his neck and ran those same warm fingers over her cheek. "I think it'll be okay. I was careful."

"Careful?" Gina stepped back away from his fingers because she had the sudden urge to throw herself against his warm bare chest and let him tell her everything would be fine. She formed a stiff smile. "Well, I'll let you know how it turns out." She turned and headed in the direction she thought would lead her to the front door of his apartment.

She'd taken two steps into the courtyard before Jackson caught her. "Hey! Wait a second! We need to talk about this," he said.

"No, we don't. I'll take it from here. Thanks for an evening to remember."

"Don't leave yet," he said, his voice so compelling she felt herself waver. "Come back inside." Gina took stock of where they were, standing in the middle of a public place in the chilly January air that neither of them was dressed for, and the idea of going back inside gained merit. Then she thought of Emma waiting at Courtney's, and Courtney's mom who'd probably already considered calling the police.

"Look, I've got to go. I have a daughter and I need to pick her up." She gingerly tried to pull away from the hand that firmly gripped her arm, but he held on.

"How can I get in touch with you?"

"Dial 911," Gina suggested. Jackson didn't seem to appreciate her humor.

"I want to know you're okay," he said gruffly. "I'd like—"

"Gina!"

Gina heard the voice behind her and watched Jackson's expression go dark. She turned her head and saw her friend, Nick, her daughter's godfather, striding across the courtyard in their direction.

"Damn," she muttered under her breath. No time to escape or prepare. Nick was bearing down on them like one of her nosey brothers—a man on a mission. She swiveled to meet him.

"What's going on? What are you doing here?" he asked as if he had a perfect right to ask. He looked her over from head to toes as only an ex-cop and former partner would have the nerve to do, pausing briefly at

Jackson's large hand holding her arm. "Are you all right?" He shifted his suspicious gaze to Jackson.

"Good morning, Nick," Gina said with pointed politeness. "And, I'm fine." She shrugged away from Jackson's hold to prove her statement. "I was just leaving."

"*Just* leaving?" Nick repeated in surprise.

Gina looked toward Jackson hoping he would say something so she wouldn't have to. But, he crossed his arms over his bare chest and went silent. He seemed to have changed completely, from the concerned lover to a wary stranger.

Peripherally, Gina saw Nick's love, T. J. Amberly, step out of her front door into the cold. God, all Gina had done was spend the night with a stranger. It was supposed to have been anonymous, ships-passing-in-the-night sex that no one else would ever know about.

At this rate, the whole story would probably appear on the front page of morning edition of the *Atlanta Times Union*—complete with pictures.

"I really have to go now," Gina said taking a step backward. She had to get away from the inevitable questions from Nick and T.J. . . . and Jackson. She had too many of her own to deal with. "I'll talk to you later," she called to everyone in general and made good her less than graceful escape.

As she pushed through the door to the public section of the building, Gina nearly collided with a man who seemed to be supervising the cleanup after the party the night before.

He hurriedly apologized, then looked at her in question. Gina was used to that look. When she wore her uniform, people treated her differently. She watched as his gaze shifted past her toward the courtyard for a second. Then he smiled.

"Happy New Year," he said, brightly.

Gina stared at him for a moment, trying to figure out what he meant by that. "Yeah, right," she said under her breath and headed for the sanctuary of her car.

GINA WAS GONE by the time Jackson yanked on his boots and followed. After scanning the parking lot, he returned to the building and let the outside door slam shut behind him.

"Has anyone mentioned to you that it's thirty-eight degrees outside?" Jackson recognized the voice. When he turned to face Tyler, the building manager, he felt like growling. He certainly wasn't cold. "No wonder she left in such a hurry. You look like a renegade—unshaven with no shirt." He shook his head, then continued, "I thought when you cut that ridiculous ponytail off, you had come to your senses."

Tyler's rebuke, on top of his own frustration, pushed Jackson over the edge. He raised one hand and pointed a menacing finger in Tyler's surprised and perfectly groomed face. "I may never shave again. And if you want to survive the day, stop talking. Now." He waited a full minute to test Tyler's will to live. Then he lowered his arm, opened the courtyard door and walked through it. He savored the blast of cold air that surrounded him, until he caught Tyler's parting words as the door closed.

"Happy New Year to you, too."

3

"HAPPY NEW YEAR, Mama!" Emma exclaimed as Gina walked into the playroom of Vickie Cameron's home. Vickie's daughter Courtney piped up with her own, "Happy New Year."

"Happy New Year to you, too," Gina said with every ounce of enthusiasm she could muster, hugging Emma close. Even though the year seemed to be starting out in utter chaos, some things remained solidly the same, like her responsibility and love for her daughter.

"I'm so sorry I'm late," Gina said to Vickie, as she released Emma.

"Oh, don't worry about it. They've been entertaining each other. All I do is feed them occasionally." Vickie slanted her a speculative look. "So, did you have a nice New Year's Eve?"

Gina hadn't taken the extra time to return to her house and change clothes, so she still wore her uniform. Vickie knew her shift had ended at eleven o'clock the evening before. Gina ran a hand through her hair and sighed. "I need coffee," she pleaded.

"This way." Vickie pulled her toward the kitchen. "I just made a fresh pot."

Gina gave in and allowed Vickie to cluck over her, getting her coffee and fixing her some cheese toast, just like she would do for Emma. By the time her friend finally took the seat across from her at the table, Gina was ready to talk.

"I did something really stupid last night," she said. She could tell she had Vickie's complete attention.

"What did you do?" Vickie asked. "Quit your job?"

"No, I—" Gina stopped to glance down the hall toward the playroom and listened for a moment, checking to make sure the girls were occupied. Vickie leaned closer.

"I spent the night with a total stranger," Gina blurted out. Then she sighed and rested her forehead on her hand.

"Are you all right? You look like you've been mugged." Vickie sounded concerned, yet her question actually made Gina laugh before she caught herself.

Mugged? Sort of. But not hurt. Not by any stretch of the imagination. Unless they'd made a baby...

"No. I'm fine, I guess. I just can't believe I did it."

"Who is he? Where did you meet him? Are you going to see him again?"

Gina looked at Vickie and tried to decide what to tell her. They'd gotten to be such good friends over the past year that Gina knew she could confess anything. But this…Jackson… Gina couldn't bring herself to go into detail. Some of those details, like the fact that Jackson had taken her to a couple of very pleasurable places she'd never been before, made her uncomfortable. Other details, such as the motorcycle parked in one room of his loft and the fact that he was definitely the wrong man for her, a widow, a mother and police officer, to get involved with, were too embarrassing. The whole thing had been a one-night stand; nothing more. Vickie would never meet him, Gina would never have to present him to anyone.

"I met him at a party," Gina said, answering the second question because it was safer. Because she didn't want to think about why she might *need* to see Jackson again. "I went to meet Nick, and Jackson was there."

"Jackson?" Vickie tried out the name as if it would speak for the man. "So, Nick knows him?"

Oh, my God. In the scramble to get to her daughter, Gina had put Nick and his inevitable inquisition out of her mind. Nick knew more about Jackson than she did. And, now, Nick knew that she'd spent the night in Jackson's loft.

"Sort of," Gina answered noncommittally. She rubbed her forehead. "Do you have any aspirin to go with this caffeine?"

JACKSON PUSHED OVER the kickstand of his bike and rolled forward out of the gate. The distinctive growl of the Harley's engine calmed his anger somewhat. As he picked up speed, the cold January air bit into his exposed skin. It was too damned cold to ride a motorcycle. But, he decided, a little pain might do him good.

He couldn't believe the last twelve hours. Not only had he broken several set-in-stone rules he'd adopted about sleeping with women he didn't know, he'd been called to account for it by Nick DeSalvo with T.J. looking on.

He hadn't been in the mood to make excuses, so he'd walked away. And now, he was riding away...to think.

How could he have been so stupid? He should have asked Gina about birth control. He should have used a condom like he always had. The idea that from the moment he'd touched Gina, nothing had gone like it *always* had made him edgy. He didn't like complications. He knew from past experience how a moment of stupidity could lead to a world of complications. How one night with a woman could produce a child.

Gina had said she had a daughter. Jackson's mind shifted to his own daughter, the one he'd never met except on the day she was born. She'd be . . . nearly ten. He wondered if she looked like him, or more like her mother. He'd forced himself to think of her as healthy and happy, and he hoped she didn't hate him for stepping out of her life. At the time, everyone had been in agreement that she was better off without a hard-headed delinquent for a father. And a mother who wasn't emotionally ready to raise a child.

Now ten years later, his life was just the way he wanted it. Uncomplicated. He did what he pleased when it pleased him to do it—no wife, no kids, no one digging around in his choices. A renegade, as Tyler liked to point out. He'd even managed to put the past to rest. Or so he'd thought.

Damn.

He hadn't put anything to rest. He'd only been asleep at the wheel and ended up taking the same asinine chance.

His hands felt as if they'd been flash frozen. He'd forgotten his gloves. Another stupid mistake. He gunned the throttle of the big bike and roared faster. The sound of the engine suited his anger, his frustra-tion. Putting his life in the hands of fate wasn't part of the plan. But then he'd never run into someone like Gina before. Someone who aroused all those protec-tive instincts he considered hazardous to his life-style. He didn't want to care about her, about a stranger, but he did. And he knew he had to see her, to know if they'd done something irrevocable on New Year's Eve.

Hell. He didn't even know how to get in touch with her, other than asking Nick DeSalvo or T.J. And he'd be damned if he'd open up his life to anyone's opinion or discussion. This was between him and Gina.

He could always do as Gina had suggested and call the police precinct.

That thought brought him screeching to a halt. As the bike idled between his thighs, Jackson ran a hand over his face under the visor on his helmet. Had he actually had sex with a police officer? The irony was too ridiculous.

He'd thought, according to pop psychology, he was supposed to be attracted to women who were like his mother. Well, he loved his mother but he'd never run across a woman like her. Probably because he'd always run with the dangerous ones, out of the mainstream, "normal" world. What he had to offer had little to do with marriage or commitment.

He didn't advertise it, but his father had been a cop. A tough-as-nails, unforgiving, go-by-the-book cop. And because of that, Jackson had rebelled and made his own rules early on. This was too kinky even for him. He'd slept with a cop, shimmied her right out of her blues . . . and he'd enjoyed it, more than he wanted to admit.

He had a couple of friends from the old days who knew how he felt about cops and authority. They would never let him live it down if they found out. He cranked the bike up again and shot forward, sending up a spray of gravel. Maybe if he rode long enough, he'd freeze the memory of last night right out of his mind. He'd be too cold to remember Gina's heat, too busy to worry about babies, about yesterday and tomorrow, too tired to wonder if he'd ever get the opportunity to touch her again.

GINA OPENED her front door and wasn't surprised to find Nick on the other side. He'd given her a five-hour head start but, now, it was time to pay the piper. He looked so serious, she couldn't resist a playful jab.

"Happy New Year to you, too, dear." But he didn't smile or reply. They stood for a long moment with only the sound of the New Year's Day parade on television playing in the background. "Come in," she added, finally, and moved aside.

By the time they'd walked down the hallway, Emma met them at the far end dragging her favorite doll by its one remaining arm. A pair of plastic handcuffs dangled from Emma's wrist.

"Hi, Uncle Nick."

"Hi, you," he bent to give her a quick hug.

"Come and see my new police car. It's just like Mommy's."

"I will in a minute, sweetie. I need to talk to your mom right now," he said, obviously preoccupied.

"It has a real light— And a siren—" Emma dashed away toward the playroom.

Gina decided to let Nick deal with Emma's attention without interfering. Emma wanted to play show-and-tell and Gina definitely did not, especially when she knew the conversation would be about Jackson. Nick grasped her arm lightly and steered her toward the kitchen.

"Want some coffee or a soda?" she asked, stalling for time.

"I'll take coffee," he answered and released her arm. Before he could settle into a chair at the kitchen table, Emma returned with her police car.

"Here it is. Look." Emma squatted and placed the car on the linoleum floor at his feet. She fumbled with a switch under the back bumper and the red light on top of the car started flashing and the tinny imitation of a wailing siren filled the air.

"That's great," Nick said as he sat down.

Gina glanced at him as she filled the coffee maker with water. The siren was enough to set anyone's teeth on edge but Nick seemed to be surviving. Gina set out cups along with cream and sugar, then waited.

"Why don't we turn the siren off now?" Nick suggested to Emma.

She pushed the car forward until it rested against the toe of his shoe then raised it to fumble with the switch.

Something clicked but the siren kept right on wailing. Emma opened her small hand before looking up at Nick. She held out the piece of plastic that used to be the switch. "It broke." Tears filled her eyes and the siren wailed.

"Let me see," Nick said. "I'm sure we can fix it." He took the car from her and flipped it up to look. "First we have to turn it off." He tried to fit his large fingers into the tiny slot without success.

"Have you got a screwdriver handy?" he asked Gina.

The next fifteen minutes were spent stopping the siren and fixing the switch. Nick had to remove the batteries to silence the noise and, with Emma in his lap to watch every move, he superglued the switch back together.

His cup of coffee had gotten cold before he'd made Emma happy. Gina had been content to let him deal with the siren emergency—because that meant he couldn't grill her about Jackson. But she could tell his patience was being tested—not with Emma but with her.

"Okay, Em, let Uncle Nick drink his coffee," Gina said, reaching to help her daughter down from Nick's lap.

Nick looked at his watch. "I'm going to have to go soon and I—"

"No, don't go yet." Emma changed her mind about getting down and snapped the free part of her handcuff around Nick's wrist.

He gave Gina a helpless look of exasperation. "Don't tell me she lost the keys to these."

Emma giggled. "Now you have to stay forever—under arrest."

"I don't remember them having keys," Gina said as she reached for Nick's wrist. "Let's see..." Emma's arm rose along with his. Gina looked down at her daughter and gave her a conspiratorial wink. "Hmm. You might have to stay forever."

Nick made an attempt to pull away so he could look at the cuff himself, but Gina didn't let go. "Oh, here it is." She pushed a button and the cuff opened.

"Okay, that does it," Nick growled in a menacing voice. "Anyone who handcuffs me gets tickled...." He proceeded to tickle Emma until she shrieked louder than the siren. Then he stood up with Emma under one arm like a sack of potatoes. "After that," he threatened, "I lock 'em in the closet."

"The closets are full, Uncle Nick," Gina said. "How about taking her to the playroom," she offered helpfully.

Nick left the kitchen with Emma squirming and laughing. Gina followed. After they got Emma settled, handcuffed to her doll, watching the video of her choice, Gina walked Nick down the hall toward the front door.

"Well," Nick began. "I wanted to talk to you but I can see that it isn't going to happen today." He stopped to face her. "Just tell me one thing about last night. What were you thinking? I know you must be lonely but you don't have to—"

"Nick—"

"I know, you're an adult, but—"

"Nick!"

His features settled into a frown. "You know I worry about you."

Gina looked at her former husband's best friend and felt a stab of guilt. Nick had always been there for her, even after Mike died. Especially after Mike died.

This week Nick had nearly been killed by a crooked cop—a man they'd all worked with. And Gina had had to sit and listen to her dead husband's voice on tape confessing to a series of crimes. There would be another trial and the past, never far from the surface, would be dredged up and sifted through, again. Nick had enough to worry about.

"I know you worry, but it's time I started looking out for myself."

"Why? I'm not going anywhere and this thing with Jackson—"

"You have T.J. to look out for now," she said quickly, hoping to stop the questions once and for all. "And I won't let you waste one more moment of your happiness worrying about me." She sighed and raised one hand to touch his jaw. "I've never forgiven myself for ruining your career. You were the best cop I've ever known and that includes Mike. If I'd known the price you'd have to pay for helping me, I never would have agreed."

Nick looked away for a few seconds, then patted her hand. "Well, if you'd confessed to lying at the inquiry, both of us would have gone to jail for perjury." He smiled slightly. "Nice job of getting me off the subject, though.

"Listen, I have to say one thing to you—and not because of Mike. Jackson helped T.J. when we needed him but he's a loner—not someone you'd want to depend on. He's not in it for the long haul. Be careful, okay?"

Be careful... She'd already made the mistake of trusting Jackson to be careful and now she'd have to wait for the outcome. And she had to accept that she might have to face that outcome alone. At least Nick hadn't threatened to rough Jackson up...yet.

"I promise, I'll be careful," she answered. She'd never meant it more in her life.

"I TOLD YOU to be nice to her." T.J. faced Jackson with her hands firmly planted on her hips. "But I didn't mean for you to drag her off and . . ."

"I didn't *drag* her anywhere," Jackson said as he tossed an empty soda can toward the garbage. "She's an adult, I'm an adult—"

"Nick is ballistic."

Jackson faced T.J. "I don't give a rat's—" He stopped and rubbed his face. He was beginning to lose his temper and he didn't like the feeling. When had his life become an open book? He should tell T.J. to mind her own business and show her the door. But no, that might hurt her feelings. That's what happened when you let people get too close. They started to give advice, run your life—introduce you to *their* friends.

He should have never been friendly to T.J. Then he wouldn't care what she thought of his life-style, of him, of the way he did or didn't treat a woman. The way things were going, in a week or so she'd have him dressed up in a suit taking flowers to Gina. He sighed loud enough for T.J. to get the message.

"Look, tell Nick not to worry about it. Whatever happened is between Gina and me. And that's how we want it." He had no idea how Gina wanted things but he'd included her anyway. Then an uncomfortable thought struck him. What if he never saw her again?

Because of Nick, or because of the way they'd parted. He didn't like the feeling that accompanied that idea.

"What are you going to do about her?" T.J. persisted.

"What do you mean, *do*? You want to know my intentions?" His intentions were honorable to a point, but he didn't like being grilled about them. If he and Gina had made a baby, he had a right to know.

"Are you going to see her again?"

Jackson thought about it for a moment, then he made a decision. He'd never put too much effort toward chasing women, but he *would* see Gina again, whether she liked it or not. Once. He wanted to look into her eyes and hear her say yes or no.

"Yeah, I am, even though it's none of your business. And you can tell Nick—"

T.J. held up a hand to stop him. "I'll work on Nick," she said with a half smile. "Just do me a favor? Be careful. She's important to him and he's important to me."

The ringing of the doorbell to his loft interrupted any caustic comment Jackson might have made about Nick. Like directing T.J. to tell him to butt out.

"What now?" he said, crossing the room. He opened the door to Tyler.

Tyler waved jauntily to T.J. and faced Jackson with a Cheshirelike smile. From the first day he'd become building manager, Tyler had been an unintimidatable pain in the rear. Most of the time Jackson appreciated his quirky single-mindedness and his nerve, but sometimes . . . Right now, he was glad to have an interruption. Talking about or, rather, explaining his private life to anyone, even T.J., made him twitchy.

"We need to borrow your van to take the bottles and cans from the party to the recycling center." In his usual fashion, Tyler had demanded, not asked.

"Fine," Jackson said and moved toward the counter that divided the living area of his loft from the kitchen. Tyler followed him partway and plucked the empty soda can from the top of the trash.

"Happy New Year, T.J.," he said.

"Same to you. Make any resolutions?" she asked.

Jackson turned in time to see Tyler frown like a pained man as he contemplated the can in his hand. "Every year I resolve *not* to give another New Year's party. My services are severely underappreciated."

"It was a great party," T.J. soothed. "Some of us even got lucky."

Jackson hoped she was referring to herself, but when he looked up after snagging the keys to the van off the counter, both of them were looking at him.

"A police person, no less." Tyler grinned. "The law and the Neanderthal. Whoever would have thought . . ."

"I don't want to talk about this," Jackson interrupted and tossed the keys in Tyler's direction.

Tyler caught the keys one-handed and smirked. "Personally I think it's a vast improvement."

Jackson flinched inwardly. He knew that tone of voice. He prepared himself for one of Tyler's lofty observations about life.

"Have you ever taken a good look at most of the women you bring home?" Tyler started the ball rolling. "They might be every heterosexual boy's fantasy but they're not exactly the stable type."

"Take the keys and get the hell out of here, Tyler," Jackson grumbled, knowing by the other man's obvious enjoyment that he wasn't finished yet.

T.J. laughed and Tyler looked at her like a coconspirator. "I know I shouldn't speak ill of the newly departed, but Steve and I have a bet about Rita." He shifted his gleeful gaze to Jackson before continuing. "We think she's a vampire.

"Have you been excessively tired since she left? Or found any unusual marks?" Tyler squinted and moved forward as if he intended to examine him and Jackson lost it. He was tired of being the subject of a conversation he didn't even want to have.

"Out!" He pointed to the door. "Or, I'll throw you out."

"No wonder you don't have any friends. Anyone ever tell you that you look like Arnold Schwarzenegger when you're mad?"

Jackson made one threatening step toward him and Tyler folded.

"Thanks for the keys," he called airily and waved. "Bye T.J." He winked in Jackson's direction. "Only time will tell."

4

"ALL RIGHT, THAT'S IT." The shift sergeant picked up the papers in front of him and pushed himself to his feet. "Be careful out there," he said mimicking the old "Hill Street Blues" sentiment.

Gina gathered up her leather gloves and stood to move along with the other officers filing out of the room. Her life had fallen back into its normal routine after the holidays . . . after New Year's. She was glad. She'd had enough excitement already for the year. And, she still wasn't certain if there would be any consequences from her flight of fantasy with Jackson.

Sometimes right before she drifted off to sleep she could almost feel his hands on her body, hear his low voice whispering her name. Fantasy. Gina had to deal with the real world, she didn't have time for fantasy.

And, she didn't want to think about him. She'd pushed his image out of her mind by working hard and staying busy at home. She'd gone from worrying to wondering, then moved on to denial. She decided to pretend it never happened. If the night they'd spent together never happened, then she wouldn't wonder if he ever thought of her, or if he cared whether or not they'd made a baby.

One of the male officers in front of her, Greg Taylor, pushed open the outer door to the county parking lot then waited for her to go through. Chivalry wasn't dead in this new, politically correct world, it just had a new agenda.

"So, how's your love life, Gina?" he asked as she moved past him.

"Very funny, Greg." She used his name in the same snide tone he'd used hers. "And, none of your business."

"Maybe you should just give it up and go out with me," he said, letting the door swing closed and moving up behind her.

"Maybe you should take your wife out instead," she replied without sparing him a glance. It was an old game, one he'd perfected and she'd learned to deflect. But for some reason, tonight she felt more vulnerable. Thank goodness Greg wasn't her shift partner.

Then she saw a man, on a huge black motorcycle. Her pulse made an uneven lurch before it pounded faster.

Jackson.

He looked like Hell's own angel, balanced on the Harley he'd parked in the no parking zone. Dressed in black, muscle-hugging, leather pants and a heavier leather jacket that protected the upper part of his body, he seemed to fill her vision and block the horizon. She couldn't help staring. Nor could she believe that over the space of almost a week she'd forgotten so much about him. Or rather, remembered it wrong.

If she'd been forced to describe him for a lineup, her first word would be dangerous, the second would be riveting. Jackson was the kind of man who would make any woman stare and . . . wonder. Her gaze dropped to the shiny black helmet resting on the seat between his legs.

Gina didn't have to wonder. She knew what it would be like to touch him, to be touched by him. In direct contrast to the cold January air, her face warmed in response to her memory of Jackson's playful mouth, his warm, talented hands . . . his firm thrusts inside her.

The muscles of her stomach clenched yet her legs felt rubbery. Gina's feet halted of their own accord as she met his cool-blue inspection.

The two officers walking a few steps ahead of her stopped near the front of the bike. As she watched, Jackson swung one long leg over the back and stood. His left hand tugged the zipper of his jacket down and opened it, as if he intended to stay awhile.

"Nice bike," one of the officers said.

"Thanks," Jackson replied without taking his eyes off Gina.

Gina was sure that any second he would call out to her and a taste of panic made her briefly consider turning around and hiding in the station house until he left. But, somehow she knew he wouldn't leave without speaking to her.

"You waiting for somebody?" Officer Taylor asked Jackson in an official sounding voice.

Jackson's gaze shifted to him and Gina stepped forward. "He's waiting for me, Greg," she said, forcing the words out before Jackson could answer, confessing to their connection before he did, even though she knew it would only increase the speculation surrounding his appearance.

Greg gave her a disapproving look, then turned back to Jackson. "You know you're parked in a no parking zone?"

"I'll handle it," Gina said and stepped past Officer Taylor in order to get between him and Jackson. She pretended she couldn't feel Taylor staring at her back and coming to his own conclusions. As soon as the other policemen were out of earshot, she asked Jackson, "Why are you here?"

Even though she was standing on the sidewalk, Jackson still seemed to tower over her. He needed a shave and the dark scruffiness of his jaw seemed to intensify the blue-gray intensity of his eyes. He looked every inch the bad boy, as if he'd put on his attitude with his clothes. So different from the man who'd held her in his arms.

"I came to see you."

Gina's heart rate, which had already hit the red zone, suddenly went off the scale. "Why?" She saw exasperation flicker in his eyes before he slowly ran his gaze over her from head to toe.

"I wanted to see how you're doing," he answered.

"It's barely been a week, I don't know anything yet," she said, trying not to sound defensive. "That's what you're asking, right?"

"Part of it," he said. He frowned into the air over her shoulder, then looked back. "How have you been?" he asked in a straightforward, yet subdued voice.

The question seemed sincere and it took Gina by surprise. She hadn't really believed that their one night together would still be on his mind, except for the baby issue.

"I've been good—busy," she said. The sound of a horn punctuated the words. Gina looked past Jackson and waved to her partner, Russell. "Be right there—

"I really have to go," she said.

Jackson ran a hand through his unruly hair and then rested it on the handlebar of the Harley. "Tell me how to get in touch with you—" he looked toward the police car idling in the parking lot "—other than showing up here."

"Come on, Gina! We need to roll," Russell called out.

"Why don't you give me your number," Gina suggested, thinking of the safest solution. Meeting here was safer than seeing him alone. She knew she couldn't trust herself with him alone—not after New Year's Eve. "I'll call if there's a problem."

Jackson reached in his back pocket and pulled out his wallet. "Call either way," he said and handed her a card. "I don't like the way things were left between us."

Gina took the card without touching his fingers, yet just being so close to him sent a shiver of awareness through her. She remembered his fingers on her skin, running through her hair, gripping her hips. And she remembered that he'd given her what she'd wanted on New Year's Eve—one night of fantasy.

"Me, either," she agreed, watching the angle of his mouth...remembering. "Listen..." Suddenly she couldn't think of one witty thing to say. So she gathered herself together and took the first step away from him. "Thanks for your concern," she said.

Thanks for your concern? Gina flinched as she slid into the passenger seat of the patrol car. What a dumb thing to say. It sounded like something you told the school counselor when your tomboy daughter had been caught tying up the class bully.

She changed the angle of the rearview mirror in time to see Jackson's Harley roar forward and make a sweeping left-hand swing through the parking lot. A man alone, facing the world. An image from a movie she'd seen, of Rutger Hauer as the black knight charging into a fight on an ebony stallion sprang into her thoughts.

When the motorcycle headlight flashed in the mirror and the dispatcher's voice crackled over the radio, she snapped out of it and picked up the mike. "Unit 3-4-0 in service," she said as they rolled out of the parking lot and into the real world.

She glanced at her partner and saw his smirk. "Don't even start, Russell," she ordered.

JACKSON STOMPED through the door of his studio, slamming it closed. Well, that hadn't worked out worth a damn. He'd known it was iffy for him to show up at the precinct but he'd been out of options. And he'd needed to see her. To see her reaction, to gauge if she'd missed him or even thought of him since New Year's. He didn't like to give that admission too much thought.

He hadn't found out what he wanted to know. She'd been professional, distant, while he'd tried to keep everything casual and low-key. But there had been too many distractions, too many people getting in between them. It seemed that the world was conspiring to keep them from ever being alone again.

The cops who worked with Gina were certainly determined to protect her. They'd treated him the way he'd always been treated by upstanding citizens of the community—with contempt. Why should he think that anything had changed? He was an avowed loner. He'd stopped trying to prove himself worthy years ago. The cost was too steep. Besides, his time and effort hadn't worked.

And he was past the point of worrying about it now. A week ago, on New Year's Eve, he'd had his life planned out just as he wanted it. He and Rita had called their on-again, off-again alliance off—for good. When he'd lifted a toast to the New Year, he'd had no attachments, no pressing responsibilities other than the projects he chose to take on, and no reason to please anyone but himself.

And then he'd run into Gina.

He'd pleased her and himself in the process. Now it felt as though all hell had broken loose. Suddenly everyone wanted to know his business. Nick, T.J. and of course the brave men in blue wanted to keep him away from Gina, for her own good. Because he appeared to have nothing to offer her but what they'd already shared—a hot night in his bed. And that made him want to see her all the more.

And she could be pregnant.

Remembering the look of panic on her face before she'd walked out of his apartment New Year's Day, he wearily rubbed a hand over his eyes and bent to pick up a hammer resting on the concrete floor near his workbench. How could he have been so stupid? He wasn't a kid anymore. After what he'd gone through with Lauren, why the hell had he— The hammer clattered as he tossed it onto the workbench with his other tools. He knew why. He just didn't like the answer. He'd lost control. He'd broken his own rules, and now he would have to deal with the consequences.

And that meant Gina had to deal with him sooner or later. Jackson looked at the date displayed on his watch. Monday, January sixth. If she didn't call by Thursday, he'd figure out how to catch her alone again if he had to corner her on the street. Then she'd have to let him have his say about their future, or arrest him for harassment.

JANUARY SIXTH. Emma's birthday was only five days away and Gina still hadn't finalized the party arrangements. While part of her thoughts remained tuned in to the chatter coming over the radio, the other part made plans. Vickie had offered to help cook and put up decorations, but Gina needed to come up with something special for Emma's seventh birthday.

She'd started the first grade in the fall, and Gina knew she'd be excited that her friends from school would be there along with Courtney. Now Gina just had to figure out some way to entertain them.

"You hungry?" Russell asked as he turned the car toward a line of fast-food restaurants.

"Sure," Gina answered without much enthusiasm. She had gotten tired of fast food a long time ago, but since they were officially always on duty, fast food remained the only option. Something they could take with them if they were interrupted by a call.

As they made the turn onto the five-lane highway, Gina blinked in surprise. A car was riding in the wrong lane, coming toward them. Fast.

"Russell?"

"I see him," Russell replied and began to slow the patrol car. He blinked the headlights to wake the other driver up to his mistake.

The car kept coming.

"Damn!" Russell said under his breath.

Gina realized what he meant. He had nowhere to go. A car beside and slightly behind them on the right kept him from swerving in that direction. All he could do was hit the brakes, lay on the horn and hope the other car stopped or swerved.

At the last moment the driver in the other car finally woke up and swerved in panic. But, by that time, he couldn't miss them. Gina put her head down and braced herself for impact. She thought of Emma...and the brief glimpse of a knight on a motorcycle flashed through her thoughts. The final thing she heard before the grinding crash was a heartfelt obscenity from Russell.

5

THE WEATHER turned warm for January. The temperature outside had risen to a balmy fifty degrees. Jackson shifted on the lawn chair, closed his eyes and drew in a deep cool draft of air. January seventh, around four in the afternoon. Not that he was keeping track.

He'd spent the day working up a plan for a project an old client of his wanted him to take on. A resort near Charleston. They wanted a new look for a restored brownstone. Distinctive, atypical ironwork instead of the usual wrought iron. The budget was substantial and Jackson had been assured total freedom. But, used to working on larger projects, he'd been reluctant to accept the job, even though the client was a friend.

This morning, waking up alone and unaccountably grumpy, he'd decided he needed to stay busy. He had a lot of things to do. After giving the plans his best shot, he'd worked out in the weight room, made a few phone calls, and tried not to think about Gina.

Why was he so fascinated by her? Because she didn't seem to want anything to do with him? Why was her touch, her smell, the way she looked with her hair spread across his pillow engraved on his mind? Just the thought of her made him warm and restless.

Even the uniform hadn't turned him off. Nothing sexy about a uniform, unless you were the one close enough to know what lay beneath it. The soft skin, the warm welcome, the breathless heat.

He wanted her again. And, it rankled that she seemed to have no such desire. She had two more days to call before he went after her, literally. Then she'd have to make a stand one way or the other.

He sat quietly for a few moments, rerunning parts of the night with Gina through his memory. The winter sun, a weak imitation of summer heat, warmed the skin of his face. He heard the low jangle of the wind chimes across the courtyard brushed by the wind. And something rustled in the shrubbery near him.

A bird, probably a pigeon, he decided but didn't open his eyes to look. The rustling got closer. He heard a door open and a woman's voice echoed through the courtyard.

"Emma?"

Jackson opened his eyes and looked into the chocolate brown eyes of a little girl standing about a foot away from him. She stood staring at him, her hands stuffed into a navy blue jacket that had St. Pious embroidered on the front. A plaid skirt and knee socks finished off what had to be a school uniform. He blinked, but stayed perfectly still so as not to scare her. Where in the world had she come from?

"My name is Emma," she said gravely, then reached for his hand. Before he could react, she snapped the open end of a set of handcuffs around his wrist and said, "You're under arrest."

Jackson couldn't stop a smile. She certainly wasn't scared or intimidated by him. "Okay, I give up. You caught me," he said. Over Emma's shoulder, Jackson saw T.J. cutting across the courtyard toward them.

"You have the right to remain silent," Emma continued. "And we're going to have to call your mother."

"Emma!" T.J. reached them, looking so serious that Jackson wondered what was up. Did she think he would be mean to a little girl? He shrugged off that reaction and tried to kick start his sense of humor again.

"Are you here to bail me out?" he asked when T.J. stopped next to them.

"Sorry about this," T.J. said, squatting to get a closer look at the handcuffs. A half smile played around her mouth. "Nick warned me about these."

"He's under arrest," Emma insisted and pulled Jackson's hand toward her.

"But he's not a bad man," T.J. reasoned. "This is a friend of mine. His name is Jackson."

Emma turned serious eyes on him. "Do you break crayons or squirt milk out of your nose?"

Jackson stifled a laugh. "No, never. Well, at least not in a long time," he assured her.

Emma's gaze darted away for a moment, then returned. "Do you have any kids?"

Before Jackson could answer, T.J. reached for the handcuffs and changed the subject. "Your Uncle Nick just called and he's going to come pick us up soon. I've fixed you a snack. You need to eat before we go to see your mom."

T.J.'s features went serious again. Jackson wasn't sure he wanted to hear what was coming next.

"Emma is Gina's daughter," T.J. said with a warning look.

Gina's daughter. Something inside Jackson's chest tightened. He studied Emma's face as if he might see Gina looking back at him.

"My mommy's in the hoppspital," Emma told him, stumbling over the word.

Jackson heard himself breathe out the question, "Why?"

T.J. found the button for the handcuffs and the side entrapping Jackson's wrist fell free. She looked into his eyes. "She was in a car accident last night on duty. She and her partner were hit head-on."

"She's not gonna die," Emma said, sounding slightly unsure.

T.J. reached for her hand. "No, honey. She's going to be fine. She just needs to let the doctors fix her leg."

"Which hospital?"

"Piedmont," T.J. answered and tugged Emma toward her.

"Can he come and have cookies with us?" Emma asked.

"No, not right now. Jackson is busy," T.J. hedged.

"He doesn't look busy," Emma stated.

T.J. looked at him helplessly, but the only thought in Jackson's mind was getting to the hospital. He had to know how badly Gina had been hurt. A car wreck—of all the things that could happen to a police officer...

"Can't you come, please?" Emma asked again and stared at Jackson.

He didn't have the guts to say no. "Yeah, sure." He pushed to his feet and expected her to step back from him because of his size. Instead, she reached for his hand to pull him along.

IT REALLY WASN'T FAIR, Jackson decided almost an hour later as he sat on the couch with Emma in his lap listening to her read a book aloud.

She'd wanted to read to him. He hadn't asked her, or forced her to tell him about her mom. But, he felt guilty just the same. When he'd decided to corner Gina, he'd never planned on making friends with her daughter in order to accomplish it. It seemed a little underhanded to him.

But Emma was damned hard to resist. She came at you with wheels spinning. You had to either catch her or let her roll over you. And there didn't seem to be a cowardly bone in her body. He'd thought that most little girls were shy. Not Emma.

But then again, what did he know about little girls? He hadn't been around when his daughter was Emma's age. He hadn't shaped her life and seen her personality take form. He'd never even been this close to a child, experienced sticky fingers on his hands or watched her in action, acting as if she'd decided she could do anything. And she didn't need to be helped.

Gina's daughter. He wanted to see Gina, to find out more about her injuries than T.J. had been able to tell him, but he wasn't looking forward to explaining to Gina how he'd met her daughter and become her new best friend.

A key rattled in T.J.'s front door and before Jackson could make a graceful escape from Emma's immediate vicinity, Nick DeSalvo walked in. After kissing T.J. hello, Nick moved into the hallway and stopped to stare at Jackson and Emma with a hard look in his eyes.

Emma glanced up, then slid off Jackson's lap and bolted across the rug in Nick's direction. "Hi, Uncle Nick!" Emma called and launched herself into his arms.

"Hi, sweetie," Nick said, keeping his unfriendly gaze locked with Jackson's.

Left holding the book, Jackson actually experienced a jab of envy. He hadn't asked for Emma's complete attention, but losing it made him want it back.

"Can we go see Mommy now?"

"We sure can, in a couple of minutes. Okay?" Nick answered.

"Okay." Emma turned. "This is Jackson. He's T.J.'s best friend."

Best friend? Jackson glanced at T.J. and inwardly winced. When he looked back, Nick's frown had shifted to a scowl and Jackson decided he needed to hit the road. He stood and tossed the book near Emma's backpack.

"I was just leaving," Jackson said, relieving Nick of the opportunity to ask him to go. He knew Nick was protective of Gina and that would certainly include Emma—not to mention T.J.

Jackson didn't want Nick as an enemy. But, he also couldn't resist a jab. "I'll probably see you at the hospital." Then without giving Nick time to reply, he glanced down at Emma. "See ya later, shortstuff."

"I TOLD YOU, if you had a problem to call."

Startled, Gina opened her eyes and stared into Jackson's unsmiling face. He wasn't dressed in black leather this time. He had on a denim work shirt and faded jeans. She felt nearly naked in her thin, hospital-issue gown.

"Well, I—"

"Damn," he added as he sized up the cast on her right leg below the knee. He looked as though it hurt him more than it did her. "What happened?"

Gina's voice failed her for a moment and she wondered how her heart had gotten lodged in her throat. Of all the painful excitement she'd gone through for the last twelve hours, Jackson's appearance in her room might finish her off. When she didn't answer right away, he moved closer to her and lightly touched the bandage on one side of her forehead.

His voice lowered to the intimate level she remembered so well from the one night she'd spent in his arms. "What the hell happened?"

The concerned sound made tears come to her eyes, and she had the urge to turn her cheek into his hand. She blinked and tried to shrug it off. It had to be the pain medication making her emotional. There was no reason to cry. The worst was over, yet . . .

"Just one of those things," she joked, but her voice sounded distraught even to her own ears.

His fingers lightly brushed through the hair near her bandage. "Do you have a concussion?"

"A slight one." Gina pulled away from his touch and swallowed to get herself under control. She couldn't think straight when he was touching her—she'd already learned that lesson. "A piece of glass or metal cut me. I think they said they put in six or eight stitches. It's not as bad as it looks," she added, making an effort to smile.

She didn't know why, but she couldn't stand the thought of him thinking of her as helpless. Even if she had been lying there worrying, wondering about how she could do her job. About how she could take care of Emma on crutches.

His hand dropped away and he turned his attention to the cast on her ankle once more. "What does the other guy look like?"

"Better than me. He was treated and released right after the accident." Gina shifted slightly to find a more comfortable position flat on her back. "My partner got a broken nose from the air bag. Most of the impact was on my side of the vehicle."

"I'm surprised you didn't arrest him," Jackson said.

If she'd known him better she would have guessed he was teasing. She decided to take the chance. "Well, I told Russell to shoot him, but he was more concerned about his nose bleeding all over his new uniform shirt."

Jackson's hard mouth slanted into a crooked, begrudging smile and something inside Gina eased. It felt good to see him. Nice to know he gave a damn. No matter how dangerous the admission might be, she'd never have to tell anyone.

A commotion in the hallway drew her attention. Nick pushed the door open and ushered Emma through as T.J. followed, her arms full of flowers. Emma's eyes looked as big as saucers and Gina's heart dipped.

"Mama?"

"I'm here, honey."

Nick let go of Emma's hand and she rushed toward the bed. Gina angled one arm to touch her and also to deflect her from the cast on her leg. To her surprise, Jackson put out his hands to catch Emma midstride.

"Let me lift you up," he said. And, without hesitation, Emma went into his arms.

Gina was nearly shocked speechless. Jackson had had the same effect on her. He'd put out his strong arms and she fallen into them. In that instant, she decided she really needed to have a discussion with her daughter about talking to, and touching strangers. Especially strange men. But, before she could recover, Emma looked at her from the haven of Jackson's arms and said, "Mama, this is my friend Jackson. He lives at T.J.'s."

For a full moment, there was utter silence in the room. Gina glanced from her daughter to T.J., who seemed suddenly to be totally consumed by flower arranging. Nick stood frowning in Jackson's direction.

"Can you go home now?" Emma asked unperturbed and leaned toward her. Jackson carefully lowered her until she could sit on the side of the hospital bed.

"No, honey," Gina answered, willing to ignore the rest of the undercurrents in the room. "I have to stay a little longer."

"You'll be home for my birthday, won't you?"

"Your birthday?" Gina shut her eyes a moment.

"I'm having a birthday party," Emma said, explaining to Jackson.

"You know I wouldn't miss your party, Em," Gina assured her even though she had no idea how she'd be able to give a birthday party in her condition. She'd have to ask Vickie....

"I talked to your sergeant," Nick said from the other side of the bed, and Gina was grateful for a change of subject. "He's going to arrange for workmen's compensation. But you know what that means ... not even light duty. Until you can hold up to regular duty, you're on vacation."

"Some vacation," Gina answered.

"We need to talk about getting someone to help you at the house. And that costs money—"

"Nick." Gina had to stop him. She couldn't sit there and discuss her financial situation in front of a room full of people. "My mind isn't clear enough to make any decisions yet." When he just scowled at her, she added, "It'll work out. Don't worry."

Don't worry? What a joke. She couldn't believe she'd said that. Hadn't she just spent the last couple of hours lying in the hospital bed, worrying? And now she had to add the logistics of a birthday party to the hurdles in front of her. It'll work out. Yeah, right.

"So, Emma—" in desperation she shifted the subject "—how did you like staying at Uncle Nick's last night?"

"He let me watch Bart Simpson."

Gina turned a quelling motherly stare toward Nick. "Oh, he did, did he?" Behind her, she thought she heard Jackson chuckle.

At that moment, a nurse pushed open the door and stopped short. "You know there are only supposed to be two visitors in here at one time," she informed them. "And we're moving another patient out of recovery into this room, so we may have to shorten the visit."

"I can wait outside," T.J. offered, then looked at Jackson. "Jackson?"

Gina watched the look on Nick's face and felt like smiling for the first time that day. He seemed absolutely green at the idea of T.J. leaving with Jackson. She figured he was a grown-up—he could speak for himself.

"Thank you for the flowers, T.J. They're beautiful."

"You're welcome. I thought you could use an early reminder of spring." T.J. smiled then looked toward Jackson. Nick stepped closer and took her arm.

"We can both wait outside. Let me know when Emma's ready to go," he added with his gaze on Jackson.

As the door closed behind Nick, T.J. and the nurse, Emma chattered on. "You want me to read you a story?" She made an attempt to shrug out of her backpack. Suddenly Jackson's big hands were there to help.

Gina didn't know what kind of expression she wore but when their gazes met, Jackson handed the strap of the pack to Emma as if it were on fire.

Fifteen minutes later, nearing the end of the story, the nurse returned. "I'm sorry, but your husband and daughter will have to leave now. We have to get the new patient settled."

Her husband and daughter. There was no way Gina could look at Jackson after that statement. Correcting the nurse would only make things worse. So, she drew Emma into her arms and kissed her soundly. "I miss you so much," she whispered into her hair.

Emma's fingers twisted into the sheet. "Come home soon, Mama." Her tomboy's voice sounded younger, babyish—afraid, and it twisted Gina's heart.

"I will. I promise." As she released her daughter, she found her gaze locked with Jackson's.

Again, without hesitation he reached for Emma . . . and she went to him willingly. Gina's eyes filled with tears but she wasn't even sure why. She just knew she couldn't speak.

An echo of pain crossed Jackson's features and he gingerly set Emma down on her own two feet and handed her the backpack. But, he didn't pull away when she curled her fingers into his hand.

"We'll be back," he said as if in warning.

"Okay," Gina whispered.

6

IT WAS THE FIRST TIME he'd seen Gina out of her uniform, except when she'd been in his bed. Without the intimidating blues she'd seemed softer, younger. About as tough as her daughter—until he'd touched Emma. Then she'd looked at him as if he were some kind of child molester. Jackson rubbed his hands on a shop rag and tossed it, a little harder than necessary, in the general vicinity of the rag bin.

If she thought so little of him, what would happen if they'd made a baby on New Year's Eve?

The same thing that had happened last time, his dark inner voice informed him. She'll take the baby or give it up and you'll be alone.

That was what he wanted wasn't it? To be alone, to run his life as he pleased, without having to answer to anyone. He wasn't the marrying kind. Sure, he'd give her money. In the years since he'd made a name for himself, he'd put aside money for the child he'd never known. Just in case.

But he couldn't imagine giving up a child like...Emma. Emma reminded him of himself as a kid, rushing at life head-on without stopping to think about the consequences. A few years and a few hard knocks would curb her enthusiasm, he thought sagely. A shudder of recognition shocked him. God, he sounded just like his father.

Jackson wished he'd finessed some information out of T.J. or Nick. He wondered what kind of man Emma's father was, and how he could leave her and Gina. For a moment, he imagined finding the guy and punching him in the face. Because Emma wasn't tall enough to do it. And because she needed a father to protect her from herself.

Jackson popped the igniter for the welding torch, flipped down his visor and started cutting metal. This is where he belonged, in his own world. The heat and the sparks and the jagged cuts matched how he felt inside. He didn't want to think too much, to care too much because he'd always be the outsider. Normal life not required. And nothing he could do would change that fact. He'd roamed too far off the beaten track to find it again. He'd learned to make his own path.

THE DOORBELL RANG as Jackson pulled on a clean pair of jeans. He glanced at the clock on his dresser. Three-thirty. Before he made it to the front door, the bell rang again twice.

Emma was in the act of reaching to push the bell one more time when he opened the door. Jackson had to hide his smile. Her school uniform looked as if she'd been wrestling in it. Her mostly white shirt was untucked and the knees of her socks were darker than regulation.

"Jackson," she said as if his name was magical.

"Hey, Emma," he replied, and before he realized it his hand moved out to touch her hair. He drew it back quickly and glanced at T.J.

"Can we come in?" Emma asked and stepped forward trying her best to see past him.

"Hold it," T.J. said and clamped a hand on Emma's shoulder. "I thought you wanted to invite Jackson to my house." Jackson watched T.J.'s gaze skitter across his bare upper body before she looked down at Emma. "This is probably a bad time for a visit."

Jackson squatted down to Emma's level. She didn't seem interested in talking to him. Instead, she rose on her tiptoes to look over his shoulder. He turned to see what she had found so interesting. The blue neon calligraphy was the brightest thing in the room.

"Do you have any toys?" Emma asked. She leaned so far forward that she lost her balance. One of her small hands came to rest on his arm.

He glanced upward to see if T.J. noticed before answering the question. "Only grown-up toys."

Emma graced him with a hopeful gaze. "Can I see?"

If she'd been taller and older, it would have been easy to say no. He'd been saying no to women for years who tried to push their way into his life—for his fame, his money, his attention. But he'd never been the focus of such fearless trust . . . except for the night with Gina. She'd trusted him until . . . He shrugged. "Sure." As he pushed to his feet, Emma squeezed by him into the living area of his loft.

"Wait here a minute, okay?" he instructed. T.J. reached for Emma's hand to keep her from touching anything. "I'm going to get a shirt and some shoes."

When Emma made a move to follow him, T.J. tugged her back and rolled her eyes in exasperation. "Where are those handcuffs when you really need them?"

"Sister Cecile took them away, remember?" Emma said answering the rhetorical question. "She said I can't have them back until Mommy comes to see her."

Jackson had to smile. He thought of the way she'd handcuffed him and the way she'd just bullied her way into his loft. His smile disappeared. Someone needed to have a talk to Emma about being friendly with strange men. Come to think of it, Gina needed that same exact lecture.

As Jackson pulled on a T-shirt and slipped his feet into a pair of shoes, he realized that being around normal people was having an odd effect on him. It caused him to revert back to the manners and rules his parents had made in their house.

You never came to the table barefooted or bare-chested. You never treated a woman with anything other than respect. And you never trusted strangers.

By the time he returned to the living area, Emma had found his motorcycle.

"Will you take me for a ride?" she asked as she poked the tire with one curious finger.

"No. Sorry. This is one of those adult toys," Jackson answered. "Have to wait till you're taller." He purposely walked past her. He wasn't getting talked into something Gina would really kill him for.

"But I—" Emma began.

"You want something to drink?" Jackson asked T.J.

Emma tore her attention away from the motorcycle long enough to answer with her own request. "Can I have soda?"

"Let's see what I have," Jackson hedged. What did he know about feeding kids? But, somehow, he didn't think a lot of sugar was good for them.

As he reached the refrigerator, he felt a push on the back of his leg and Emma crowded in next to him to check out the contents.

"I have soda—" he decided not to mention the beer "—and milk." He pulled the milk container out, unscrewed the cap and sniffed to make sure. Then, he opened the cabinet over the refrigerator and snagged a bag of cookies.

"Chocolate chip," Emma supplied. "Can I have soda, too?"

"How about this, you can have soda, or cookies."

Emma's good humor seemed to fail. She reached for the cookies. "These are my favorite."

"Hey, that's what you said yesterday about the cookies at my house," T.J. said behind them in a teasing voice.

"Those are my favorite too," Emma went on, unflappable.

"Well, you can have cookies and a glass of milk. Deal?" Jackson asked.

"Okaaay," Emma agreed and walked away looking dejected but keeping a tight grip on the bag of cookies.

As they settled down at the counter for cookies and drinks, T.J. changed the subject.

"You know, I just thought of something. Nick and I both have to be downtown on Friday. We're giving depositions for the trial and we've been trying to figure out how to get Emma home from school. . . ." She pinned Jackson with a calculating look.

"Since you and Emma already know each other—"

"Uh, I don't think that's a good idea," Jackson hedged, remembering the way Gina had looked at him when he'd touched Emma.

"You busy on Friday?"

"No, I, uh—"

"Of course I'd have to talk to Nick about it. He's been so busy preparing for the trial and with work, and now Gina's accident, we hardly have time to say hello and goodbye."

Jackson didn't want to say anything negative about Uncle Nick in front of Emma so he solved the problem another way. "I think you'd better talk to Gina before you make me the designated driver."

RUSSELL, GINA'S PARTNER, had just launched into a story about Officer Taylor trying to get a cat out of a tree without drawing his gun when Jackson pushed open the door to her hospital room.

Dressed in leather again, but just the jacket this time, Jackson hesitated at the door. He seemed surprised. Visiting hours were almost over. He must have waited for Nick and Emma to leave, Gina realized. He'd obviously expected to find her alone.

"Hey," Jackson said. His gaze slid from Gina to Russell as if he thought they might ask him to leave. When they didn't, he walked farther into the room, past Russell and stopped at the foot of her bed.

"And, you would be . . . ?" Jackson began without preamble. He'd shifted into his attitude again, and the tightness of his jaw made Gina nervous.

"Russell, this is Jackson . . ." As Jackson stared at her and waited, Gina's mind went completely blank. The sudden memory of lying next to him in bed rather than looking up at him had scrambled her logic.

"Gray," Jackson added, supplying his last name.

As Gina watched the two men shake hands, she managed to add, "Russell was my partner. He was in the accident, too."

"Nice shiner," Jackson said, his mouth twisting, relaxing slightly.

Russell self-conciously raised a hand to the tape over his nose. "Yeah, well, I guess it's better my face than hers. I was already ugly."

In the next moment of awkward silence, Jackson unzipped his jacket and shrugged out of it. Gina had to drag her gaze from his broad shoulders and ignored the impulse to comb her fingers through her hair. She turned to Russell.

"Did Greg call the fire department to get the cat?"

"Nah. The tree wasn't that tall. A neighbor turned up with a ladder, so up Greg went." Russell laughed. "He got out of it with a few scratches and a broken watchband. The Sarge told him that from now on he should just carry a can of cat food.

"Then, of course, everybody had to tell a bigger and better animal story. Hey, remember the time Mike put that mangy dog he found wandering down the freeway in the back of his patrol car?"

Gina smiled. "How could I forget? After what the dog did, he stopped by the house and raided my cleaning supplies."

"It took three days for the smell to go away." Russell laughed again. "Yeah, I sure miss Mike. He was a hoot. A damned good cop, too," he added then seemed to catch himself, as if he shouldn't have brought the subject up. He glanced in Jackson's direction, then at his watch.

"Well, I guess I better be going," he said to Gina. "I'm glad to hear that you're getting out of here tomorrow. I wish you were coming back to work."

"Me, too," Gina said in wholehearted agreement.

"Nice to meet you," he said and nodded to Jackson before patting Gina's arm. "The guys all said to say hello. Call if you need anything, okay?"

"I will. Thanks, Russell."

With Russell gone, Gina had no excuses. She squared her shoulders as best she could while lying on her back and faced Jackson. He was looking at the empty bed next to hers.

"What happened to your neighbor?"

"Went home," Gina replied.

He looked at her then. "And you go home tomorrow?"

"Yes, finally." Gina breathed a sigh of relief. "I can sleep in my own bed. . . ." She shifted slightly trying to get more comfortable. The muscles in her back felt frozen in place.

This was the first time they'd been alone since New Year's Eve. Jackson's blue eyes seemed bluer than she recalled and for a few seconds she just stared into their depths before forcing herself to remember what she needed to discuss with him.

Gina knew she couldn't wait any longer to get things straight with Jackson. About Emma, and what he expected from Gina.

"So, Emma asked me if you could pick her up at school tomorrow . . . on your motorcycle."

"I never told her I'd pick her up," Jackson said, looking uncomfortable. "T.J. mentioned that she and Nick had to go to court and . . ."

Gina ran a hand through her hair to push it back. God, she hated being helpless. How was she going to take care of Emma and herself if she couldn't even drive a car?

"I told them to ask you." He appeared uneasy with the whole idea—defensive. "Oh," he added, "and the motorcycle was never mentioned."

"I had a feeling that part was Emma's idea." Gina couldn't stop a smile. "You should have seen the look on Nick's face—"

"I would never hurt her," Jackson said stiffly.

Gina stopped smiling. He looked as if she'd accused him of something. "I didn't think you would," she said. She didn't, not really. That feeling of safety she'd experienced during their one night together returned. "But she only has me to look out for her . . . and Nick," she continued. "And I know she's a little—"

"Not a little—" Jackson interrupted "—a lot. She comes at you like a freight train with no brakes. No fear." He moved closer to the side of the bed and rested one large hand on the metal rail. "Where's her father?"

Gina had to swallow once before she could speak. Even after all this time, the words were difficult to say. "He died three years ago," she answered. Something stopped her from telling him how. From telling him that Mike had committed suicide. She didn't want Jackson to think Mike had been a bad father . . . or husband, because she didn't believe he had. She still didn't believe he'd taken his own life and left them alone.

"That was Mike?"

The memory of the last time she'd mentioned Mike to Jackson rolled over her, shutting out the past. He'd been on top of her at the time, his warm weight holding her down, skin to skin. And they'd just . . . Gina felt her face grow warm. By the look on Jackson's face she knew he was thinking of the same moment.

"Yes," she murmured and lowered her gaze to the sheet covering her. She shifted her upper body, trying to find a more comfortable position then automatically pulled the sheet upward and smoothed the edge with one hand.

"How?"

The question caught her off guard. She hadn't thought he'd want an explanation. Death was death. She looked him in the eye again. "What difference does it make?"

"I want to know. Your partner makes him sound like some kind of hero."

"He was a cop." Did that qualify as a hero? Probably not, but he'd been her husband...her hero. "He was shot." *With his own gun.* She couldn't say it. Couldn't face a battery of questions from yet another source. "He died on Christmas Eve, a few weeks before Emma's fourth birthday."

After several heartbeats of silence, Jackson's hand tightened on the railing near her. "I'm sorry," he said. He sounded angry rather than sorry, and Gina couldn't bring herself to ask him why. She put her head back to rest her neck and ended up staring at the ceiling tiles.

Suddenly, Jackson braced an arm on the railing and leaned over her to look into her eyes. "I'm sorry I brought it up," he said, frowning down at her.

"It's okay." Gina felt the prick of tears. His apology was unexpected—sweeter for making its way through his defenses. "I'm not upset at you," she admitted. "It happened a long time ago and I— Emma and I are doing fine. At least until all this happened." She shrugged and then grimaced. "I'm just tired of this place, tired of not being able to turn over. My back feels like it should be in a cast." She brought one hand up to rub the moisture out of her eyes. "Maybe I should ask for more drugs," she added, only half teasing.

"I give great back rubs," Jackson offered.

Gina's hand froze in midswipe. He didn't look as if he were kidding. The bad boy had disappeared, replaced by the man she'd given herself to New Year's Eve. "Uh, no, that's okay." She remembered his hands, warm and sure. But she didn't think this was the appropriate time for those thoughts, or to get reacquainted.

He gently touched the piece of tape on her forehead with two fingers. "It's not like we're strangers."

She stared up into his hard, unsmiling face. "But we are strangers." She couldn't help pointing out that small fact. Just because they'd been naked together, had passionate sex, didn't mean they *knew* each other.

"You know I can make you feel better—" When she didn't answer he went on. "And don't worry, I'm not gonna climb into this bed with you."

He rubbed a thumb lightly over her eyebrow. "Come on. Let me do *something* for you." His voice had that low, intimate tone again, the one that made her warm from the inside out. The one that made her want to crawl into his arms and surrender. He took her lack of refusal as a yes. "You want to sit up? Or try to roll over?"

"I'll sit." She shouldn't be doing this, Gina thought. But a few moments later he sat behind her on the bed, his strong hands kneading her shoulders through the thin barrier of her hospital gown and it felt like heaven. She sucked in a breath and flinched when he hit a particularly sore spot.

"Sorry," he said but kept going, working the sorest places a little harder.

Gina let her head drop forward and surrendered to his fingers and palms. This is better than flowers, she thought fuzzily. His hands moved lower and Gina heard herself whimper in sheer pleasure. Almost better than . . .

The announcement in the hallway that visiting hours were over barely made a dent in her awareness. The longer he worked her muscles, the warmer his hands got. She could hear the rush of his breath, feel the warmth of it. She felt safe and pampered and *better*. A few moments later, a nurse pushed open the door and peered in. Gina jumped as if she'd been caught doing something illicit, but Jackson steadied her and continued to rub the line of her spine.

"Visiting hours are over," the nurse said.

"Need about five more minutes, okay?" Jackson asked.

"Okay, five minutes. That's it," the nurse agreed then left.

Gina didn't know if Jackson had smiled his killer smile, looked threatening, or if the nurse just took pity on her. Whatever the reason, she was grateful. For the first time since she'd been brought into the hospital, she felt relaxed. So relaxed that when Jackson smoothed his hands over the length of her back then stopped at her shoulders, she slowly leaned backward until she was lying against him. In a natural movement he brought one arm around her to hold her upright.

She let her head fall back to rest on his shoulder as if they'd been in bed together a hundred times. She didn't want to move, to think. She only wanted to rest there, warm and sleepy with his arm around her.

"Thank you," she whispered.

"Maybe you'll be able to sleep now." His voice rumbled near her ear. "And when you wake up, it'll be time to go home."

For one crazy moment, Gina wished she could simply sleep there, in his arms like she had New Year's Eve.

"Jackson?" She didn't open her eyes or move but the words came tumbling out. "When they brought me in after the accident, they asked if I could be pregnant." To his credit, Gina thought groggily, he didn't move or flinch. He held her as if he'd stay all night if she asked him to. "I told them I didn't know." She felt as though she were slipping away, holding on to wakefulness by the very real touch of his chest and his arm. "They gave me a test, but it's too soon. I still don't know."

"It's okay," he answered, close to her ear.

She thought he must have kissed her, near the bandage on her head, but it was so fleeting . . . more of a breath than a kiss. The thought made her smile sleepily. Such a big, dangerous man, afraid to kiss too hard. Why did he hide that fact from everyone but her? She thought she heard him say, "Go to sleep." But she was already drifting away.

7

"JUST EXACTLY WHAT is it that you can't take about me?" Jackson said in exasperation.

Nick DeSalvo's unfriendly gaze faltered for a moment. "Look—" he shoved a hand through his hair "—this is a family thing. As far as I'm concerned, Gina and Emma are my family and they've got enough problems without someone like you barging into their lives."

Someone like you.

The cold air around Jackson seemed to go colder. After leaving Gina, he'd cornered Nick in the courtyard of the Coach Works to tell him he would pick her up and take her home from the hospital. It rankled to have to argue about it. He should have asked but that wouldn't have changed the answer he got. No, without explanation. Damn, he could have gotten that much from Gina.

"So, Mike died and put you in charge?" Jackson asked. "Don't you have enough to do with your important job? And the court case? And saving the world in general?" The words were a blind defense, something he might have used in his younger years in arguments with his father. That thought made him even madder. "And where do you get off looking down your nose at *someone like me?*"

Nick looked ready to commit murder but Jackson didn't care. He didn't want to know why this had suddenly become so important to him. But, it had. And he'd be willing to fight—even someone he respected, like Nick DeSalvo—to get what he wanted.

"That's right, my buddy Mike died, and left me to look out for Gina and Emma. I take it seriously," Nick answered in a low, furious tone.

Jackson looked away, regretting his choice of words. He hadn't intended to bring *the husband* up. The hero. Mike might be dead, but his ghost seemed to be very much alive and standing right in the center of Gina's life.

He faced Nick down armed only with the truth. "I'm sorry about your buddy. But, Gina's still alive . . . and she trusted me . . . enough to spend a night in my bed." He crossed his arms giving Nick the first shot if he wanted it. When Nick didn't take it, Jackson relaxed slightly.

"Think about it. I care about her. She needs help right now and I'm volunteering."

Nick seemed undecided, so Jackson pressed forward. "You want to check me out? If that's what it'll take, I'll give you my damn social security number."

Nick shook his head, but looked more amiable. "I already have your social security number." His mouth shifted with obvious amusement. "I just haven't used it yet."

Jackson couldn't believe it! But before he could say anything, Nick continued. "You and Gina. I don't get it. The two of you couldn't have less in common if you lived on different planets. She's as straight as an arrow and you're so elusive, you're almost invisible." He gave him a long searching, unreadable look. "You're not just doing this because you want to tick me off? Because I hassled you before, when I first met T.J.?"

"Sorry to disappoint you, DeSalvo, but this doesn't have a damned thing to do with you. Besides—" Jackson smirked "—if I wanted to tick you off . . . I could always become T.J.'s best friend."

Nick surprised him by smiling. "I shot the last guy who put his hands on her. Believe me, you don't want to 'make my day.'"

"You're right," Jackson answered. He remembered. He'd been there that night. He'd seen the look on Nick's face when he'd heard T.J. had been kidnapped. "And if you're worried about me being around Emma, then fine—you pick her up from school. I have the van and what I *want* is to drive Gina home from the hospital."

"Do you always get what you want?"

"Pretty much," Jackson answered.

They faced each other silently for several moments.

"Gina said she'd call me when the doctor releases her," Nick began. "Her friend Vickie is supposed to get Gina's house straightened up, buy some groceries, then meet us there. She's keeping Emma tonight and taking her to school in the morning. I have to go to work, to the courthouse, then pick up Emma." He paused, then looked darkly at Jackson.

"I'll call you in the morning when she's out," he said as if it killed him to give in.

"I'll be here," Jackson replied and uncrossed his arms. It looked as if he wouldn't have to fight after all.

GINA MADE IT from the wheelchair to the van under her own power . . . barely. By then, the new crutches felt as though someone had driven wedges of metal under each of her arms, and the brisk January breeze had found its way through the lightweight sweatpants that had been cut to accommodate her cast. The dull throb under the cast on her ankle reminded her not to even think about putting it down. Bed rest and crutches for at least a week—doctor's orders. Then they'd discuss a walking cast.

By the time she'd reached the van, she'd begun to tremble from either the exertion or the cold, and she lost her balance slightly. From directly behind her, Jackson's big hand shot out to steady her. As she breathed her thanks, she looked up at him and tried to find her good humor. She thought she'd been hallucinating when he'd sauntered into her room this morning. What had Nick been thinking when he'd sent Jackson in his place? Why did his presumption make her so mad?

And why had she been so happy to see him?

Jackson tossed the paper bag that contained her ruined uniform through the side door of the van. "Here, hold on to me and give me the crutches." Balancing herself between the van and Jackson she watched as he propped the crutches against the sliding door. Then he moved closer and slid an arm around her. Before she could protest, he lifted her into his arms, ducked his head and placed her on the back seat.

"You okay?" He stood there looking at her, concern etched in his features. Little did he know that her sole worry had to do with her body's reaction each time he walked into a room or . . . touched her. The memory of his hands working the muscles of her back the night before warmed her.

"I'm fine," she lied. She couldn't tell him that he scared her to death. God, here she was with a broken leg and all she could think about was asking him to put his hands on her again. This celibacy thing must have pushed her over the edge. Any man would probably affect her that way, she quickly asserted.

But she couldn't lie to herself. She worked with men every day, she'd met doctors and interns during her hospital stay. None of them affected her the way Jackson did. Of course, she hadn't been naked with any of them. . . .

"I figured you'd have more room in the back. You still have to wear your seat belt though." His eyes challenged her to refuse. "It's the law."

Before she could answer, he slid the door closed.

The ride to her home was awkward but uneventful. Jackson drove like an eighty-year-old, not too fast, no sudden turns or stops. Sitting on the bench seat in the rear of the van meant Gina could watch traffic and street signs or stare at the back of his head and wonder what he might be thinking.

"Thank you for doing this," she said finally.

"No problem."

Searching for something innocuous to say, she murmured, "Emma will be disappointed that she missed you." Gina had meant it as a backhanded compliment—safer to talk about Emma's feelings than her own—but as she said it, she realized it was true. Emma would be disappointed. She'd gotten attached to Jackson.

Emma needed a father, Gina thought guiltily. A father and a normal life. And Gina needed . . . Her mind flipped through rosy images of married bliss from the movies and they seemed to overlap with Jackson carrying her in his arms. She sighed. Her life scored closer to the TV show, *Cops*. The music from the opening credits chanted through her thoughts . . . *Bad boys, bad boys. . . .*

That led her memory straight to the night she'd spent in Jackson's arms. Hot sex, motorcycles and leather. *Bad boys . . .*

"Were you that fearless when you were little?" Jackson asked.

"Me?" The question caught Gina off guard. She clamped down on the adults-only image of she and Jackson and dutifully thought back to her childhood. Her life had been so different from Emma's—she'd had a big family close around her. "I suppose, but in a different way," she answered. "I had three brothers. I learned how to stand up for myself." She laughed as she remembered her father forbidding her older brother Vince to hit her—no matter what she said or did. She'd used that to her advantage all the way through high school.

"And Emma's not so little anymore. She's going to be seven this week. Oh— You need to turn left at the next light."

As they pulled into the driveway of her house in the suburbs, Gina inwardly sighed in relief. The house that had seemed so empty after Mike died, now seemed like a haven. She couldn't wait to get inside and really relax. But she couldn't relax around Jackson. And she felt uneasy about bringing him into her home. Not afraid . . . just not ready. He belonged in her fantasies, not in her living room, or her bedroom. Or her real life.

Jackson pulled the van as close as he could to the front walk then jumped out to open the side door. He held out his arms and she let him help her slide slowly to stand on her good foot. Then he took off his leather jacket and arranged it over her shoulders.

At the end of what seemed to Gina like a two-mile crawl on crutches, her friend Vickie opened the door and stepped back. Once inside, Gina felt Jackson slip his jacket from her shoulders to give her more mobility.

"How are you?" Vickie asked sounding concerned. But when Gina looked up to answer, she saw that Vickie's attention had shifted. She was staring at Jackson. It was difficult to tell by the expression on her face whether she was in shock or awe.

"I thought Nick . . ."

"Vickie, this is Jackson Gray. Jackson, this is my friend, Vickie Cameron." After the introductions, Gina stepped forward as best she could. She couldn't worry about Vickie's reaction at the moment, she needed to sit down.

The silence behind her after Jackson and Vickie had greeted each other seemed deafening. Gina tottered slightly on her crutches as she turned the corner toward the living room and suddenly, Jackson's hand was on her arm again and Vickie was in front of her, plumping pillows on the couch. By the time she'd gotten seated, her heart was pounding like a drum. Jackson placed the bag with her uniform next to her and squatted down to look her in the eye. If she died in that moment it would be ruled heart failure. Overexposure to an overpowering male.

"Anything else you need for me to do?"

Gina couldn't think of a thing with him gazing into her eyes. It was an embarrassing fact that she didn't want to contemplate too closely.

Vickie spoke up, breaking the spell. "Are you mechanically inclined?"

Jackson turned his attention to her. "I've been accused of that."

"Well, I've been trying to take apart the shower doors in the downstairs bathroom...otherwise..." She pointedly stared at the cast on Gina's leg. "She won't be able to get upstairs to use the tub in the master bathroom."

Jackson pushed to his feet. "Lead me to it."

After Vickie and Jackson disappeared around the corner into the hallway, Gina ran a hand over her face and tried to get a grip on herself. When she opened her eyes, she glanced around her own living room and a new wave of embarrassment hit her. The room looked like a tornado had gone through it. A tornado named Emma.

Vickie had obviously straightened up a little, but there were abandoned toys under the coffee table, a child-size sweater draped over the back of a chair and a pair of discarded tennis shoes near the fireplace. Gina glanced toward the open doors of the playroom and saw that Vickie had rearranged the toy box and the small desk so that she could pull out the trundle bed.

Gina stared down at the cast on her leg, shook her head and sighed. So much for sleeping in her own bed. She and Emma would have to sleep downstairs, when all of their clothes and everything else they needed was upstairs. Her morose thoughts skidded to an abrupt halt when Vickie returned to the living room alone.

She quickly moved to the couch, sat next to Gina and grabbed her arm like a teenager who'd just seen Keanu Reeves. "Where did you say you met this guy?" she asked, breathlessly. She didn't wait for an answer. "This is Jackson, right? *The* Jackson from New Year's Eve?"

Her *New Year's Knight*. Gina felt like groaning. Instead, she patted Vickie's hand which held her arm in a death grip. "Don't get all twisted over it."

"He's so . . ." Vickie's eyes glazed over for a moment. "Big," she finished, lamely. Her gaze returned to Gina. "And when he looks at you . . . When we were both in the bathroom, I could hardly catch my breath."

Gina had to laugh. She'd felt the same way, only she'd been lying beneath him at the time.

"I don't know how you could . . ." Vickie stopped as if saying the thought out loud would be inappropriate. "He looks like the bad-boy, all-or-nothing type," she continued, then grinned. "Well— I guess I see how you could, for one night anyhow. But he would scare me to death," she said plainly.

Fear hadn't been Gina's reaction. "He's really—"

"Where do you want me to put the doors?" Jackson asked from the doorway.

In the answering silence, Gina wondered if she and Vickie looked as guilty as they felt. "The basement, I guess," she answered. "Vickie, will you show him? Oh, and look for those cake pans while you're down there. They should be in a box near the furnace, behind the Christmas decorations. Emma wants another rabbit cake for her party."

Vickie jumped up off the couch as if she'd been pinched. "Nice save," she mouthed as she walked toward the door.

Shaking her head, Gina decided it was good to be home after all. She used her arms to push herself deeper into the cushions of the couch but in the process, the paper bag Jackson had carried from the hospital slid to the floor. Gina bent to pick it up, then broke the tape to open it.

She remembered her uniform pants had been cut off her in the emergency room. Now she studied the jagged line created by the scissors going from cuff to waistline on the right side with some equanimity. And, no surprise. It reminded her of the violence of the accident, the damage that had been done to the cars, to both her and Russell. How helpless she'd felt. Then she pulled out her uniform shirt and saw the blood. Her own blood, from the cut on her head.

She could have been killed.

Dead. Like Mike. Without having the chance to see Emma grow up, to see her graduate, to give her away at a wedding. Without ever having another shot at having a normal life for herself, a marriage, a home . . . love.

She knew being a police officer was dangerous. But the scenario of being shot or attacked in the line of duty still ranked in the remote possibility department . . . if she was careful, if she was smart. The words of one of her training officers came back to haunt her.

One of the most dangerous things a police officer can do is stop on the shoulder, or in the lanes, of a freeway. You're more likely to be hit by traffic than to be shot by a fugitive.

She'd forgotten cars were lethal weapons. She ran her thumb over the county police patch on the arm of her shirt. She'd been so busy trying to be good at her job, at raising Emma, at getting past Mike's death, she'd forgotten that she had a lot of good reasons to want to stay alive.

The sound of Vickie's laughter brought Gina back to the present with a jolt. She managed to stuff most of the uniform back into the bag before Vickie walked through the door followed by Jackson. Vickie was smiling.

"I hear Emma is still at it with the handcuffs," Vickie said to Gina. "She gave up on Courtney because she figured out how to open them." Vickie glanced at Jackson and explained. "Courtney's my daughter and Emma's best friend." She lowered herself into the chair across from Gina and spoke to her once more. "Now Emma's arresting strangers. That kid will definitely grow up to be a police officer."

A shaft of fear went through Gina but she forced a smile. Emma? A police officer? Did she want Emma to grow up and be a cop like her father...like her mother?

"That particular piece of equipment won't be a problem, for a while, anyway. One of the sisters at school locked them in her desk," she said, masking her uneasiness.

"Have a seat, Jackson," Vickie offered before Gina could react.

Jackson's gaze went to Gina as if he needed her permission and she felt guilty. So caught up in her own turmoil she couldn't even be gracious. She'd just never pictured inviting him into her home. "Yes, sit," she added and started to move the paper bag next to her.

Jackson took it from her hands and set it on the end table before sitting down next to her. He stretched out his long, denim-clad legs, crossed his booted feet and folded his hands as if he meant to stay. Close enough to touch, Gina thought then pushed the image away.

"So," Vickie said. "What are we going to do about this party? I haven't bought or planned anything except the invitations. Emma, Courtney and I made them last night and she took them to school this morning." She bent and dragged her handbag into her lap. "Let's see," she said digging inside for a notepad then flipped it open. "We invited the whole class, that's twenty-two kids."

"Twenty-two?" Gina said weakly. How in the world would she entertain twenty-two kids while on crutches?

"Some of them won't be able to come, but we should plan for at least twenty."

Gina rubbed her temple and replied only half-jokingly, "Do you suppose we could get ten sets of handcuffs and hook them all together?"

"Wouldn't work—" Vickie smiled at Jackson again "—they know how to get out of them."

"How about a piñata or— What was that clown's name who came to Heather's birthday party? Bippo? Or, Bappo?"

"Hmmm." Vickie retrieved a pen from her purse and wrote on her pad. "I'll call Diane and ask her, but I doubt we'll get him on such short notice. And I don't think you want twenty kids swinging sticks in your house to hit a piñata. We have to think of something we can pull together in the morning. I have to work to-night and you—"

"I know someone who gives great parties," Jackson said. Greeted by silence, he looked at Gina. "You remember the party New Year's Eve?"

Feeling as though she'd just swallowed a piñata, whole, she could only nod. Of course she remembered the party. How could she ever forget?

"Tyler gives great parties." His voice emphasized the great part, yet as he stared at her, Gina knew he wasn't talking about decorations.

"Who's Tyler?" Vickie asked, breaking the tension.

"He's the building manager of the Coach Works." When Vickie still looked puzzled, he added, "That's where I live."

The memory of glittering stars and expensive party favors tugged at Gina. "This party is for kids, not adults. We're running on a small budget here," she said, trying not to sound defensive.

"Tyler knows how to find the best deals in town." He shrugged. "I'll take care of it."

Gina was speechless for a moment. "What do you mean?"

"I'll get Tyler to put together a party for Emma."

"I can't let you do that," Gina sputtered. "How do you know Tyler will even have time or want to plan a party for someone he's never met?"

"Believe me, Tyler lives to organize. I promise you, he'll do it if I ask him."

"Does he know any clowns?" Vickie cut in, obviously enjoying Gina's discomfort.

"Vickie!"

"Hey," she replied, smiling. "If this Tyler can come up with a party for twenty kids in twenty-four hours, I vote to give him a try."

"He can do it," Jackson said. Gina thought there should have been an, "or else," connected to his words by the sound of his voice. But then her thinking processes were immobilized by his intent gaze. "Trust me."

"YOU WANT ME to do *what?*" Tyler's voice had risen an octave.

"I need you to put on a birthday party for twenty kids . . . tomorrow."

"Have you been doing drugs?" Tyler asked waspishly. "First of all, nothing can be done that quickly. And, second of all, I don't even *know* any kids."

"I'll supply the kids, you supply the party," Jackson soothed. When there was no reply he added, "This is important."

"So is world peace, but I'm not in charge of that, either."

Jackson gripped the phone tighter, fought down his rising temper and decided the truth would be better than threats.

"This is for Gina's— The police *person's* daughter. Her name is Emma and I promised—"

"Hold it!" There was a long-suffering sigh. "Let me get this straight. You made a promise to a— How old is she?"

"It's her seventh birthday."

"Okay, you made a promise to an almost-seven-year-old kid and you need me to save your butt?"

"That's the problem. Actually, I made the promise to her mother." Jackson listened, heard silence and started composing threats he might use.

"I love it!" Tyler laughed wickedly.

Jackson knew from the laugh what would come next.

"If I do this for you—and it's a large *if*—you'll owe me, big time. Is that correct?"

"Yes," he admitted, reluctantly.

"And if I were to make a list of all the rules you break around here, such as working on that beast you call a motorcycle *in* the courtyard, we might actually manage to make some changes?"

He forced himself to grumble a little. In reality he didn't care what he had to do as long as Emma—and Gina—were happy on Emma's birthday. "Yeah, I'll read the list again."

"Not just read . . ."

"You make the party, I'll follow the rules." He could almost see Tyler mentally rubbing his hands together.

"All right, I need to know more about Emma and where and when and . . . Oh, and how much money do I get to spend? You know things done at the last minute are usually expensive."

"Get whatever you need," Jackson said, then remembered Gina's concerns about money. He didn't intend to let her pay for it, but he knew she wouldn't go along if she knew that. "But listen, Gina's isn't too keen on this idea so let's try to keep her out of it. I'll give you her friend Vickie's number. She'll tell you whatever you need to know."

"All right," Tyler said in a businesslike manner. Then Jackson heard him chuckle. "I can't wait to tell Steve."

"Tyler? Hey, thanks—"

"Don't thank me yet," Tyler cut in. "You haven't read the new list of rules for the Coach Works—as applies to Jackson Gray."

"Yeah, well, thanks anyway."

"You're welcome," Tyler replied in a sarcastic manner, but he sounded pleased all the same. "Now get off the phone and let me get this show on the road."

8

JACKSON PUSHED the door to Tyler's loft open wider with his shoulder and shoved the large box inside. "Here, I want you to take this to Emma."

Tyler looked at the waist-high box as if it might explode at any minute. "*Me* take it to Emma? Don't I have enough to do? Take it yourself."

"I'm not going."

"Of course you're going." Tyler waved a dismissive hand at him as he turned away. "Steve! Let's go. It's almost ten and I need at least two hours to set up." He graced Jackson with a frown. "Now, go put that box in the van and be careful you don't crush anything."

Just then Steve, looking resplendent in a tuxedo, walked into the living room of the apartment he shared with Tyler. "Will you fix this tie? I can never get it straight," he grumbled.

Jackson awarded him with a low whistle while Tyler adjusted his bow tie. Steve tugged at the cuffs of his shirt and frowned at Jackson.

"Great, I go from being the fabulous Lena Bright to impersonating David Copperfield at a funeral. I'm not sure I can do this magician act in a tux. I'm used to pulling scarves out of the bodice of a dress rather than from up my sleeve. What if I flub it?"

"You'll be fine," Tyler admonished as he straightened the lapels of the jacket. "The party is for six-year-olds. You can't go in drag.

"Now—" Tyler's gaze scanned the room "—we have everything loaded but the tiramisu. I'll get that."

"Tera . . . what?"

"It's the newest 'trendoid,'" Steve supplied as Tyler reappeared with what looked like an upside down cake in a bowl. At Jackson's puzzled expression, Steve added, "Does the word *trifle* have any meaning for you?"

"It's a cake?" Jackson replied in a dubious tone.

"It's more than a cake, it's an adventure," Tyler explained. "I spent all morning making it. Now, Jackson. Put that box in the van if you want it delivered."

"Where do you put the candles on a cake like that?" Jackson persisted as he lifted the box.

"You don't," Tyler replied as he went through the door Steve held open. "I'm going to float them in a bowl of water like a moat around it."

"A moat?"

"The kids will love it. Steve…don't forget the keys."

GINA PUT THE LAST few jelly beans on the rabbit carrot cake she and Vickie had put together while Vickie loaded the dishwasher. "I don't know what I'd do without you," she admitted.

"Nonsense, that's what friends are for." Vickie grinned. "Especially when the sh— I mean the *stuff* hits the fan. We've all been there. So, how's your leg holding up?"

"I'm having more pain in my shoulders and lower back from the crutches than in my foot."

"You really should be lying down—"

Just then a horn beeped from outside. "Diane isn't supposed to bring Emma and the kids back for another hour—" Vickie walked to the window to look out. "Oh, these must be our party organizers."

"Great. I can't believe I agreed to this," Gina replied, frowning toward her cast and feeling totally helpless in her own home. Earlier she'd managed to wash her hair with Vickie's help. And on her own, she'd taken a sponge bath.

Vickie turned to her with a smile. "I think you should go lie down for an hour or so and let us handle this."

"But—"

"Really," Vickie said as she handed her the crutches. "I talked to Tyler on the phone and it sounds like he has everything under control. You go lie down and I'll let you know when we're ready."

Gina twisted in her chair and used the table to push to her feet. As she settled the crutches under her arms, she couldn't ignore the most important question in her mind. "Is Jackson with him?"

Vickie peeked out the window again. "I only see two men, and neither one of them is Jackson. He'd be hard to miss."

Disappointed, but unwilling to admit it, Gina sighed. "Okay, well, if you're sure you can handle it . . ."

"I'm sure. This way we can surprise Emma *and* you."

"SURPRISE!" Vickie said an hour and a half later.

Gina blinked her eyes and stared at the transformation of her living room. She'd actually fallen asleep when she'd thought she'd only prop her leg up for awhile. Now she felt as if she might still be dreaming.

The room looked as though the local Cartoons-are-us store had had a going out of business sale. There were colorful ducks and dogs and mice cavorting on Mylar balloons, banners, flags and wrapping paper. Happy Birthday Emma was emblazoned in computer graphics over the fireplace.

"It's . . . amazing," she sputtered, then shifted her attention to the two unfamiliar men standing in the hall doorway. On closer inspection she decided that one looked vaguely familiar. He stepped toward her.

"Hi. I'm Tyler Richardson," he said in a businesslike tone. "We met briefly at the Coach Works." Gina remembered almost running him down New Year's morning, in her effort to leave after spending the night with Jackson.

"Hello." She shifted her crutch so she could shake his hand.

"And—" he indicated the other man, dressed in an expensive-looking tuxedo "—this is my significant other, Steve. He's going to be the entertainment, the Great..." He frowned at Steve. "What did you decide? Shazaam Achoo, Roger Dodger or Leonardo?"

"The Great Leonardo," Steve answered and smiled at Gina.

"Nice to meet you," Gina said. Then she studied the room again. "This place looks..." She couldn't find exactly the right word and *overdone* didn't seem to be appropriate. Tyler didn't notice her hesitation.

"Because of the cold weather we'll have to entertain them inside," he said, launching into what sounded like a sales pitch. "We've decorated the living room and set up a stage for Leonardo in the dining room. I called a friend of mine who is a father and he gave me a few suggestions for games." He turned to pick up a plastic garbage bag full of small wrapped packages. "Wait till you see the goody bags," he went on. "Oh, and we've set up refreshments in the kitchen." He dropped the bag back into place and swept an arm in that direction.

Gina looked at Vickie. Vickie seemed to be trying her best not to laugh. As Gina made her way toward the kitchen, Vickie spoke. "You can be sure, this is one party Emma will never forget."

A moment later Gina stood staring down at the perfectly matched, perfectly placed and perfectly pink napkins, forks, doilies and . . .

"It's a moat," Vickie supplied.

Gina glanced at her in warning but Vickie's face was absolutely straight. She forced her attention back to the table decorated like a magazine photo spread. A beautifully prepared trifle stood on a pedestal in the middle surrounded by a glass ring filled with water, flowers and candles waiting to be lit for the finishing touch. A mermaid Barbie sat perched on the edge.

"It's beautiful," Gina said truthfully. She envied the time and expertise it took to put something so elaborate together. Her eyes shifted to the rabbit carrot cake she and Vickie had decorated which had been relegated to a less prestigious position in the array, and she realized any future party was doomed in comparison to this. Oh well, Emma would only turn seven once.

The front doorbell rang and a door slammed, relieving Gina of having to make any further comments.

Emma's voice echoed down the hall. "Mama? I'm home. Is it my birthday yet?"

THE PARTY APPEARED to be a smashing success, if the ecstatic look on Emma's face all afternoon meant anything. They'd ended up entertaining fourteen kids and five parents, something Gina knew she could have never done alone—even without a broken leg.

The Great Leonardo did his act, and Gina thought it went over better than Bappo the clown any day. Tyler directed a game of Twister and Vickie helped the kids make s'mores at the fireplace. After Emma opened her presents, Tyler presented her with the video of a very famous pig which meant two hours of relatively quiet entertainment for the group—and for Steve, The Great Leonardo, who insisted on watching it with the kids.

Toward the end of the afternoon, Gina made her way into the kitchen to help clean up. She found Tyler frowning down at the barely touched trifle and a table that looked as if a swarm of locusts had attacked it.

"I don't understand it," he said, looking hurt. "I thought all kids would love chocolate and vanilla custard."

"Courtney loved it," Vickie said. "And every one of the mothers had some."

He seemed so disappointed Gina didn't dare smile. "The problem, I think, is that it doesn't have any icing."

"Or jelly beans for eyes," Vickie added.

Tyler shrugged and dumped the pile of used paper plates in his hand into a trash bag. "Oh well, if I ever do another one of these, I'll remember. Jelly beans and icing." He shook his head sadly at the apparent travesty of good taste.

Gina shifted her crutch and put one hand on his arm. "It was a great party, Tyler. You and Steve did a wonderful job." Even as she said it her mind added, *The only thing missing was Jackson.*

JACKSON DOWNSHIFTED his motorcycle and made the turn onto the residential street. *Suburbia*, he thought disparagingly. The kind of neighborhood he'd grown up in . . . and left when he'd chosen to live by his own rules instead of his father's.

He didn't care what her neighbors thought. He figured that the low rumble of the Harley had brought several of them to the windows to check him out as he passed. If the weather was warmer and kids were in the yards, mothers would probably be out warning them away from the street, from the bike, from him.

He hadn't been invited. So why hadn't he stayed home, downtown at the Coach Works where he belonged? Sure, he'd forgotten to give Tyler the helmet for Emma, but he could have had someone else deliver it.

He was on his motorcycle on a cool January afternoon, headed for the suburbs, because of Gina . . . and Emma. He felt left out. He wanted to know if the party had been fun, if she'd liked his present. He wanted to see happiness in Gina's eyes, see her smile . . . at him.

Damn.

He clamped his jaw to fight the weakness of wanting to please her. Why in the hell did it matter whether or not Gina was happy? He barely knew her, and she didn't seem to be inclined to get closer. As inclined as he felt. Hell, he was having a hard time thinking about anything else. He remembered how well they'd fit together with nothing between them but darkness. He remembered the look on her face when he'd been inside her, pleasuring her. He also remembered the way she'd practically run away from him the next morning after he'd messed up.

Damn. He had to stick around. What if she was pregnant?

Half a block from Gina's house he revved up the engine of the big bike then let it back down as he downshifted—making as much noise as possible. Might as well give Gina fair warning that he was in the neighborhood.

GINA HEARD THE SOUND of the motorcycle before Emma did. The video had just ended and the kids were spilling back into the living room. The party had begun to wind down.

Gina made her way toward the front of the house as the sound of the motorcycle got louder. With one last loud rev, the noise suddenly disappeared. Emma raced for the front door. Gina stopped her before she could throw it open and run out.

"Get a coat first," she instructed.

Emma turned to her with a look of pure childish ecstasy. "Mom, it's Jackson. And he brought his motorcycle!" You would have thought she'd seen Santa Claus.

"Yes, I see that," Gina answered trying to sound calm and parentlike. She looked through the glass storm door toward the man in black leather as he pulled off his helmet and fought her own rush of anticipation. By that time several other kids had gathered to look. "Get your warm clothes on and you can go outside for a few minutes." In what seemed like thirty seconds, the kids were dressed and out the door.

Gina felt Vickie move up to stand beside her as she watched Jackson shoo the children to a safe distance away from the bike. He squatted down and pointed to the exhaust pipe and lectured them about getting burned. When he pushed back up to his feet, Emma raised her arms. In one easy motion, Jackson swung her up and placed her on the leather seat.

Then he looked toward the house, directly at Gina.

She could feel her heart taking slow hammering beats as she stared back at him. She felt immobilized and mesmerized, and . . . giddy. How did he do it? How could he just show up and make her feel the way she had in tenth grade when she'd had a crush on the star member of the wrestling team? Tony Cappeletti had been a senior: heroic, dangerously exciting and completely unattainable.

Jackson Gray was heroic in a different way—heroic in the eyes of her daughter. And, as Gina had found out New Year's Eve, he was more physically exciting than any high school fantasy. And here he was standing in her front yard.

Tyler squeezed past her and pushed the door open. "Do you want Emma to open your present now?" he asked Jackson.

Gina watched Jackson frown instead of answering. He looked as if he'd rather be anywhere but on her walkway surrounded by children.

Tyler turned to her. "There's one more present for Emma to open. I was saving it for the grand finale, but since Jackson's here . . ." He wiped his hands on a towel and handed it to her. "It's in the van. Steve?" he called over his shoulder. "Give me a hand, will you?"

Some of the mothers had put on their own jackets and gone outside, and as Tyler along with Steve cut across the grass carrying a large package, everyone gathered around. Suddenly Gina felt a coat being draped over her shoulders. Vickie grinned, took the towel Tyler had left with her and opened the door. "Might as well see what's going on. Can you make it out on the porch? I'll get a quilt to put over you."

Gina self-consciously looked downward. Because of her cast she'd dressed in a knee-length denim skirt. In deference to the cold weather, she'd pulled on one kneesock to cover her uncasted leg. Just once the woman in her wished Jackson could see her dressed normally. Then maybe she wouldn't always feel so unsure around him. She shook her head. After New Year's Eve, she had the feeling he'd always be able to discombobulate her.

A short time later, settled on a chair Vickie had pulled out to the steps of the porch, Gina watched as Jackson unstrapped the first package that was about the size of a basketball from the back of his motorcycle. Emma, still seated on the Harley, ripped the paper off as he held it for her.

A neon pink helmet. Gina frowned. Jackson had bought Emma a motorcycle helmet? An uncomfortable vision of her daughter perched on the Harley as it flew down the road assaulted Gina. But it didn't look like a motorcycle helmet. When Tyler and Steve moved the bigger box closer, Gina realized what was in it.

Jackson swung Emma down from the motorcycle and her feet had barely touched the ground before she started working on the wrapping of the big box. With Tyler and Steve's help, the box soon fell away and the kids surrounded Emma's new bike.

"Mama!" Emma squealed in excitement. "Jackson got me a pink motorcycle."

"A what?" Gina called back wishing she could get up and walk out into the yard.

Gina watched Jackson correct Emma. "Actually, it's a Lotus, but that's the closest thing to a motorcycle in your size."

"Come out and see it, Mama."

Gina had already begun pushing to her feet when a shadow fell over her. She looked up into Jackson's unsmiling, unshaven face. He was playing the bad boy again. Daring her to play along in front of her friends. "Come on," he said and held out a hand to draw her to her feet. He gathered up the quilt and stuffed it into her arms before he dipped and lifted her.

The trip from the porch to the yard was breathless and too short as far as Gina was concerned. Yet, when he'd set her on her feet, Jackson had let her slide slowly with a little more body contact than necessary. The kids hadn't seemed to notice, but several of the mothers were staring at her as if she'd announced plans to get a tattoo.

"It's beautiful, honey," Gina said, trying to cover her reaction and steady herself as she gathered the quilt around her for warmth. Jackson had saved her the exertion of trying to walk with her crutches, but in doing so he'd also announced to every mother there that he had the right to touch her. And now, even though she stood on her own feet, he stayed close enough to brace her if she lost her balance.

"Can I ride it now?" Emma asked hopefully.

Gina looked from her daughter's delighted face to the other children gathered around. Emma had had so much excitement today, and Gina wasn't up to helping her learn to ride the new bike...so, feeling like the Grinch, she did what mothers always hated to do.

"No. Not right now, Emma. You have your friends here to play with and I can't help you with my cast. We'll try it out tomorrow, all right?" Emma looked disappointed and tried one more time.

"Please?" Her eyes shifted to Jackson to include him as an ally. "I know how to ride it...."

"Emma, did you say thank you?" Gina asked.

"Thank you, Jackson," Emma said, politely, but still sounded forlorn.

"You're welcome, shortstuff." Jackson hesitated, frowning, then stooped down next to Emma and the bike. "How about this? How about if you go and finish your party, and I'll try to talk your mom into letting me help you ride it later. Okay?"

Emma looked slightly more hopeful but not really convinced. "Can he talk you into it, Mama?"

Gina thought of the many things Jackson had talked her into, and the way he'd charmed Emma. She felt outnumbered.

"Probably," she said with a sigh.

WITHIN AN HOUR the party had concluded. All of the guests had left with the exception of Courtney and Vickie. Tyler and Steve had long since packed the van and, after promising to send her a list of expenses for the party, headed back to town.

Gina hadn't had a chance to talk with Jackson because of all the curious people around. She'd introduced him to the mothers present as a "friend." But it seemed fairly obvious to everyone that there was more to it than that. Friends didn't buy their friend's daughters expensive bicycles. And she couldn't let Jackson be more than a friend.

It wouldn't work, they were too different. She'd seen the confirmation of that in the eyes of the women at the party. They'd looked at the motorcycle, the leather and the attitude and saw what he wanted them to see. The bad-boy outsider who liked to shock people. Jackson wasn't the kind of man to change, and Gina realized, she wouldn't want him to be anyone other than who he really was. Attraction or not, she wasn't going to fool herself about that.

After thanking Vickie and saying goodbye to her and Courtney, Gina and Jackson were finally alone for a few moments.

"I know I should have asked you. . . ." Jackson said.

"Yes, you should have."

He was silent for several seconds. "There wasn't time. With the party today and—"

"And?"

He shifted his position in the chair and fiddled with the spoon she'd given him for his coffee. Finally he looked her in the eye. "I wanted to buy it and I figured you'd say no."

"You figured right."

The spoon clattered on the kitchen table as he let it go. "Tyler was supposed to give it to her. I wasn't going to butt into the party. I know I wasn't invited."

Gina watched him and waited but he'd finished talking. "I'll pay you for the bike—"

"Not in this lifetime." His blue eyes went icy and for the first time she could truly understand why people might find him intimidating.

She couldn't afford the luxury of being afraid. She had to know what he wanted from her, from Emma.

"Tell me why you're doing this. Is it some kind of guilt?" He looked away for a moment and she went on. "What happened New Year's Eve was—"

"Was what?" He trapped her with his gaze again and Gina lost the thread of the sentence.

"It was like my car accident. It happened, it's over and we have to go on from there."

He frowned slightly at her pronouncement. One of his hands gestured toward her cast. "Yeah, but sometimes the effects linger." Then his gaze roamed over the rest of her. "Sometimes things are never the same, are they?"

Gina knew what he was asking. But she still didn't know the answer. Caught by his gaze, she jumped when Emma spoke from the doorway behind her. "Mom? Can I ride my new bike now?"

Gina turned and held out an arm to her daughter. Emma snuggled close but kept her attention on Jackson. "Did you have a fun birthday?" Gina asked.

Emma nodded and leaned her head back against her mother's shoulder. Gina knew Emma had to be too tired to function but wasn't ready to give in. "Please, can I ride it just once?"

Gina looked at Jackson. He seemed ready to agree with any decision she made. There couldn't be more than half an hour of daylight left. And she knew, if

Jackson didn't help Emma ride it now, Gina wouldn't be able to help her later.

"Okay, sweetie—" she kissed her on the top of her head "—but only for a little while. Jackson has to go home and you've already had a big day. Pretty soon you'll need to take a bath and get ready for bed."

Jackson pushed his chair back and stood. Emma, with a new reserve of energy, reached for his hand.

"Put your coat on, Emma. And your knit hat." Obediently, Emma let go of Jackson and headed for the living room.

Instead of following her, Jackson moved next to Gina. He put out a hand to help her to her feet. "Let me get you settled on the porch again, so you can watch us."

Gina didn't argue. She'd reached the end of her endurance for crutches hours before. Now that they were alone, it was nice just to relax and let someone else do the walking. Having a reason to be in Jackson's arms wasn't something she wanted to think about. He stopped in the hall so she could grab her coat and scarf, then let her turn the doorknob before he shouldered his way through.

Cool air made Jackson's embrace feel even warmer as they moved onto the porch. He slowly lowered her legs, but instead of letting go, held her close and gazed down at her.

Emma's worried voice echoed in the hallway. "I can't fiiind my hat!"

Without relinquishing eye contact with Jackson, Gina answered, "Look in the playroom, or upstairs in your bedroom."

After the sound of small footsteps faded, the silence around Gina and Jackson seemed to thicken and warm.

He raised one hand and touched her chin. "I don't care what anyone thinks. I bought the bicycle because I wanted Emma to have a great birthday," he said, then ran his fingers along her lower lip. "And because I wanted to see you smile."

Gina couldn't have smiled at that moment if he'd been holding her at gunpoint. But he didn't look disappointed. His attention dropped to her mouth. Slowly, almost reluctantly, he lowered his face to hers and kissed her lightly. Just enough to cause her lips to part, enough to make her want more. Enough to remind her that she had to remain in control or she'd lose herself again, in his kiss, in his touch.

"Jackson . . . I—"

With a bang, Emma shot through the storm door like the house was on fire. "I found it!" she said and pounded down the stairs toward the garage and her new bike.

"Hold on," Jackson called after her as he quickly helped Gina sit in the wooden Adirondack chair then knelt and wrapped the woolen scarf around her toes that were exposed by the cast. "Where's your helmet?"

And they're off. Gina sighed as she watched Emma push the bike up the driveway with Jackson following. She knew the real reason he was being kind to Emma and staying in touch. He wanted to know if Gina was about to become an obligation. A decision or a problem.

She had to give him credit for that. He seemed to be willing to stick around and take whatever news that came. Just then, as she watched him help her daughter steady the bike, she realized she really knew nothing about him other than the way he could make her heart do cartwheels with his mere presence, or the way her skin warmed wherever he touched her. Not the normal things. Not whether he'd been married or if he had children of his own.

She hadn't thought about his family connections before. He'd seemed so solitary, so alone. And, content that way. She looked at the Harley and sighed. She didn't even know how he could afford to buy her daughter expensive presents.

What if he was a drug dealer? Or something equally as bad? She watched him patiently show Emma how to use the hand brakes and discounted that idea. He seemed too healthy and . . . normal. No, she amended, not normal. Not Father-Knows-Best or the white-picket-fence variety of normal. Yet her cop's instinct told her he seemed too up-front, too proud to be either a thief or a corrupter of kids.

And she'd put her own daughter in his hands. At that moment Emma pushed off and wobbled forward on the new bike. Gina held her breath. Emma had quit using her training wheels on her old bike years ago, but this bike was bigger and her legs didn't seem quite long enough. It also had all-terrain tires and hand brakes.

"You're doing great!" Jackson encouraged. "Just keep peddling."

Emma made several passes on the bike, getting more confident each time. Jackson smiled in Gina's direction and walked halfway down the driveway toward her. He pointed to Emma's progress. "Piece of cake," he said with an expression that looked suspiciously like pride.

Gina smiled back. Then she saw the car. Jackson appeared to see it at the same time.

"Emma, watch the car!" he called and started walking back up the driveway. Instead of whizzing by, the car slowed and someone rolled the passenger side window down. Emma had reversed directions and started back by the time the car was close enough for Emma to see a child's face and an arm waving.

"Hi, Heather!" Emma called and raised one hand to wave back. That's when she lost control of the bike.

The front wheel slipped off the pavement and a few seconds later, Emma was careening down the hill through the bumpy grass.

Gina instinctively rose to her feet, as if she could run into the yard. She'd rarely seen a look of fear on her daughter's face, but in that moment, Emma looked petrified.

"Emma!" Gina heard her own voice, but her mind was frozen. All she could do was watch. Then she saw Jackson jog over into the path of the bike, as if he could stop it by merely standing in her way. Gina flinched inwardly and waited for the collision.

Jackson didn't reach for the bike or try to stop it. As Emma flew by him he put out one arm and snatched her off the seat. Gina heard an audible "Oof" as Jackson's arm connected with Emma's chest, but she let go of the handlebars. After a moment of shocked panic, she clung to him as if he'd saved her life.

The bike continued down the hill and smacked into the side of the fence, but Gina didn't care. She limped down the steps the best she could without her crutches and headed for her daughter.

"You're okay, Em," Jackson was crooning to her. His voice sent a shiver through Gina. It was the same tone he'd used to console Emma's mother.

When Gina got close enough to touch her daughter's back, Emma automatically reached for her, to go to her, but Jackson held on. Her little arms were already around Gina's neck pulling them into a group hug when Jackson said, "Your mom can't hold you right now, Em. It'll hurt her leg." Gina unfastened Emma's helmet and slipped it off.

A voice calling her name caused her to look toward the road. Diane, Heather's mother, who'd been driving by had stopped the car.

"Is she okay?" she called down the hill.

Jackson shifted Emma in his arms so he could look at her. "You okay, shortstuff?" She nodded but her eyes were big.

"She's fine," Gina answered and waved to Diane. That caused her to falter slightly and she put a hand on Jackson's arm to steady herself. "Why don't we go into the house?" she suggested. She didn't know about the rest of them, but she needed to sit down.

Jackson slowly lowered Emma to the ground. She didn't move right away. Her gaze was on her bike resting against the fence at the bottom of the hill. Then she looked up at him. "Is my bike broken?"

"I'll check it out later, but it's probably fine. Dirt bikes are supposed to have a few scratches." He rested a hand on her head. "Now, you go open the door for me so I can get your mom inside."

When Jackson bent to pick Gina up, it seemed perfectly natural to go into his arms...to trust his strength.

She could get used to this, to having him to lean on. The thought was alarming so she pushed it away. She needed a nice normal guy, not a man with an attitude who seemed determined to do everything his way— normal or not. Well, like Scarlett O'Hara, she'd have to deal with that later. Right now, she wanted to hold on to Jackson and she needed his help to get back into the house.

9

JACKSON HAD BARELY set Gina on her feet in the living room when she began giving instructions.

"Emma, I want you in the bathtub on the double," she said as she sank down onto the couch. "And don't forget to go upstairs and find some clean underwear and pajamas, okay?"

Jackson waited with a detached sort of amusement to see if Emma would follow orders or find one more thing she needed to do. She didn't do either.

"Mom, can Jackson spend the night?"

Jackson's amusement fled. He met Gina's surprised gaze before they both spoke at the same time.

"No."

"I, uh—" he looked at Emma "—I have to go to work early tomorrow." It was a lie formulated to get Gina off the hook, although sleeping on her couch held much more appeal than the long cold ride home on his motorcycle. Sleeping with Gina would be even better.

Emma looked to her mother. "But I want him to, and it's my birthday," she complained.

"Em, you've already had enough birthday to last two years. Besides, you don't just invite people to stay over on the spur of the moment."

Jackson watched a blush make its way up Gina's neck and into her cheeks. The fact that she wouldn't look at him made him want to smile.

"Now, go on upstairs, please," Gina finished in an implacable motherlike tone.

"Don't go home yet," Emma said in one last parting shot to him before going through the doorway into the hall.

In a tired gesture, Gina ran a hand over her face and shook her head. "I swear, that kid has to be running on pure adrenaline at this point." She sighed. "And I don't seem to have even that much energy left."

"I should probably hit the road then," Jackson offered, although he didn't really want to go. That worried him. He'd been through enough pain trying to be normal for Lauren and look where that got him. He wasn't looking for a relationship now. He just wanted to do the right thing and get out of there. "I uh—"

"Stay. Sit for a minute," Gina said. "I haven't thanked you for pulling Emma off the bike. It would be really lousy if both of us were in a cast."

Jackson gingerly sat on the edge of the closest chair and rested his elbows on his knees. He felt like the bad guy again. When he bought the present, he'd never considered that Emma might get hurt. "Well, if it wasn't for me she wouldn't have been on the bike."

Gina awarded him a tired smile. "She loves it. We'll never get it away from her now. And I know you don't want me to pay you, but I have to ask. Can you afford to give her a gift like that?" She went on before he could answer. "'Cause I know that my budget would've been severely wounded."

"I can afford it," he answered. Ten bikes wouldn't put a dent in his budget, but there was no way to explain that tactfully. Besides, he wasn't used to discussing his financial situation with anyone; especially a woman that he didn't intend to get involved with.

Gina was staring at him, waiting. When he didn't elaborate, she got to the point. "What do you do for a living?"

"I build things."

"Houses?"

"No." He sat back in the chair and searched for words. He'd learned the hard way about answering questions. As soon as someone found out that people paid him obscene amounts of money to bend steel, their interest changed. It usually ended up with them wanting more from him than he was willing to give. "I work with metal. Bridges and things."

"Oh." She looked puzzled but seemed too tired to pursue the question. "Well, anyway, thank you for the bicycle—and the helmet. Do you have any kids?"

"Is this a police investigation?"

The look on her face was priceless. Surprise and then embarrassment. "Well, no, I um . . . We never talked about these things before. And, you seem to be able to deal with Emma. And I just wondered . . ."

Watching her fumble for words, he found he didn't like putting her on the spot. And for some reason, he wanted to tell her the truth. "I have a daughter, ten years old now, but I've only seen her once."

"Once?" She sounded shocked.

"Back when I was young and stupid and having unprotected sex." He frowned meaningfully at her, then continued, "I saw her on the day she was born, before her mother and her mother's family arranged for her to be adopted."

"Didn't you want her?"

Jackson crossed his arms and fought his automatic defensive nature. "I wanted her, even though I had no idea what that meant. But Lauren's family had never approved of me, and they had good reason to feel that way. I fought them the best I could with no money and no help from Lauren, but they finally convinced me the baby would be better off in a stable environment. Without a father like me."

"So, you've never seen her." Gina sounded amazed that he could live with that fact. And, he could understand her feeling that way—especially after meeting Emma. But he didn't need her pity and he was tired of being cast as the bad guy.

By the time he'd had enough money to go through the legal process, Lauren had gotten married. The records about his daughter's new family were sealed, and she'd already lived with them for five years. So, he'd decided, rather than disrupting her life, he'd just stay away. He'd used the money to start a college fund for her, in case she ever decided to look him up.

"No, not since she was born," he answered. But, he knew she was all right.

"I'm sorry, I shouldn't have brought it up."

"It's okay." He met her sad gaze and held it. He couldn't determine what she was thinking about his confession, but he knew how he'd felt about making it. "I wanted to tell you," he said.

Without warning, the whole tenor of the conversation, even the air around them changed. Jackson slowly sat forward again and watched the expression on Gina's face. If they'd been closer, he would have pulled her into his arms. There was, he realized, no reason why he couldn't stand up and—

"Mom?" Emma came around the corner dressed in pajamas with a towel draped around her neck. She moved straight to the couch and snuggled against Gina before looking at him. She seemed ready to go to sleep on her feet . . . and suddenly shy.

"You ready for bed, sweetie?" Gina murmured into Emma's hair. She nodded but didn't answer.

Jackson could take a hint. He pushed to his feet. "Well, I guess I—"

"Wait!" Emma suddenly found the energy to cross the room. She disappeared into the playroom, then a moment later returned dragging the towel with a book in her other hand. "Will you read me a story?" She held out the book to him.

"Emma, you're so tired you can hardly stand up. And, Jackson has to go home."

"Please," Emma pleaded, not looking at her mother but at him. Her eyes filled with tears and Jackson felt a suspicious twist somewhere near his heart. God, he had to get out of there.

"Em . . ." Gina made a move to get off the couch, but Jackson stooped down to Emma's eye level.

"If I read you one story, will you go to sleep?"

Emma nodded gravely. Jackson looked over her head toward Gina. She merely shrugged and shook her head.

"Okay," he answered. "Where do you sleep?" Emma tottered off toward the playroom and the open trundle bed. Jackson faced Gina. "I know, I should have asked. I hope you don't mind. One story and I'm history."

"I don't mind, if you don't. She's overtired and I'm too exhausted to fight with her. If you can get her to go to sleep, you'll be a hero twice in one day."

"I don't know how you do this 365 days a year," Jackson said, thinking that Gina was the real hero here. He couldn't imagine having someone who depended on him twenty-four hours a day.

"Luckily, days like today don't come along too often," Gina said in a relieved voice. "Thanks for the help."

Emma was busy digging through a drawer in her toy box when Jackson walked into the playroom. The two tiers of the trundle bed took up most of the available floor space in the center of the room so the desk and the toy box had been pushed into one corner. Emma left what she was doing, picked up her book and plopped down on the lower bed.

"Mommy sleeps up there because she broke her leg, and I sleep here," she said moving over to make a space for him.

The bottom bed was a good foot and a half too short for someone his height. "I'll just sit right here next to you," he said, lowering himself to the floor. No use getting cozy and comfortable. He gave Emma a stern look meant to forestall any argument, held out a hand for the book, braced his back against the bed and started to read.

A few minutes later, Gina appeared in the doorway supported by her crutches. Jackson could feel her gaze on him but he kept his eyes on the book. Emma had pushed up against his back in order to look over his arm to see the pictures. Her little hand was twisting the back of his shirt. He should have felt awkward, but in the face of Emma's total trust he was awed. How could anyone leave a child who trusted them with their whole being? He *really* needed to get out of there.

"If you can handle this, I'm going to get cleaned up and ready for bed myself," Gina said in a low voice.

Jackson glanced up at her, just for a second and nodded. Now wasn't the time to think about Gina and bed. He had to find out what happened to the spider in the story and get Emma to fall asleep so he could leave.

Jackson had a daughter. Gina ran the image through her mind trying to adjust. Of all the things she'd cast him as, a father wasn't one of them. A shiver ran up her spine. She ran a hand over her stomach. What if they'd made a baby? If they had, would she be able to give it up? Would he? He'd done it once before.

She turned the faucet on at the sink and wet a washcloth. She couldn't think about the future now. She really couldn't. She had to deal with the present—with washing her face and brushing her teeth while her back felt as if she had a metal spike shoved through the center of it.

She glanced at the tub and thought longingly of having a nice long, hot soak. After a day like today, even ten minutes would ease the ache in her shoulders and back. She picked up her watch that she'd left near the sink and limped toward the tub. Just ten minutes.

JACKSON FINISHED the second book and slowly closed it. He sat still, waiting for Emma to ask him to read another. When she didn't, he peeked over his shoulder. Finally, she was fast asleep. He'd been beginning to wonder if she'd outlast him. Or if Gina would have to take over when she came out of the bathroom. He'd heard the bathwater running earlier, but now the whole house was silent.

The silence suited him. It seemed as though he hadn't had a peaceful moment since New Year's Eve. He almost laughed. He'd been toasting his own freedom, right before he'd run into Gina. Nothing had been peaceful since.

He studied Emma's small hand resting close to his arm and wondered what his own daughter was like. Was she fearless like Emma? Did she wonder about her father like Emma must do? Or did she love the man who'd become her father?

Damn. It had been years since he'd allowed himself to...wonder. It was a useless pastime that only brought up more questions. Like why he hadn't settled down with a woman who wanted a family. His mother had asked him about it often enough. He frowned, then mentally shrugged. He'd leave the wondering to her.

Jackson set the book on the floor near the bed and braced one arm to push to his feet. But he didn't get very far. His sweatshirt seemed to be hung on something. He twisted around trying to see what the problem was, and Emma shifted in her sleep.

If he kept messing around he'd probably wake her up. Determined to get loose, he made another attempt to stand pulling harder this time. To his amazement, he heard the sound of tearing cloth and realized he'd nearly dragged Emma out of bed.

What the hell? He pulled his sweatshirt around but couldn't see what was holding him. Finally he ducked and slipped the shirt off over his head.

That's when he found the safety pin.

Emma had pinned the front of her pajamas to the back of his shirt. He couldn't stop a laugh, then realized he'd better be quiet or Emma would wake up and start the whole process over again. He got to his feet with his shirt and the safety pin in his hand. He had to tell somebody.

"Gina?" He tapped lightly on the bathroom door. There was no answer. He remembered standing outside his own bathroom door, trying to get Gina to lis-

ten to him New Year's Day. "Gina?" he called again a
little louder. "Are you okay in there?"

He heard a splash, the sound of something hitting the
floor and Gina's voice. "Damn!"

Jackson forgot all about Emma's prank. With one
hand twisting the doorknob, he gave fair warning. "I'm
coming in."

"Wait! I'm not . . ." Gina said. Before she could finish, Jackson was standing over her. " . . . dressed," she
added and gingerly rubbed her elbow. She'd put bub-
ble bath in the water but most of the bubbles had dis-
persed. Thank goodness she'd filled the tub almost to
the top.

"What happened?" he asked, as if he had a right to
know. The worry in his voice kept Gina from throw-
ing the bar of soap at him.

"I slipped. I must have fallen asleep and— Damn."
She rubbed her elbow again and tried to keep her arms
over her bare breasts.

His gaze moved over her briefly, in a neutral sort of
way until it reached the cast on the leg she'd propped
up on the edge of the tub.

"How did you plan on getting out of there by yourself?"

"I've done it before. I . . ." Gina suddenly realized that
he had his shirt in his hand. "Why are you undressed?"

His smile nearly undid her. The bathwater had gone lukewarm but the heated flush that ran under her skin made the water seem cold. The mother in her worried about him walking around her house half-dressed, but the woman in her wanted him to smile at her like that forever.

"Emma," he said.

Gina forgot about smiles and about her own precarious position. "Emma?" She could hear the alarm in her voice and tried to stay calm.

He brought one hand up and smiled again. "Don't worry, it was a prank," he said. He showed her the pin. "Your daughter has a unique way of inviting guests." He moved over her. "Come on, let's get you out of the tub."

Gina considered that for a moment. She did want to get out of the tub, and she'd already banged her elbow hard enough to bruise it by trying to get out alone. "Hand me two towels," she said finally.

He did as she asked but shook his head at her apparent modesty. He awarded her one slow, heated appraisal. "I've already seen you naked, remember?"

Gina felt like squirming under his gaze but she was more worried about touching than seeing at this point. She knew how dangerous it was for the two of them to be alone. Unable to come up with a better idea, she wrapped one towel around her injured leg above the cast to catch any drops of water, then held the second towel above the water level and gave him what she hoped was a frosty look. "Okay, I'm ready."

He shrugged off her reluctance and moved over her, bracing one foot against the back rim of the tub. Then his hands were under her arms, lifting her upward. He pulled her against his chest with only the damp towel between them and waited until she had both feet on the floor.

The only sound in the room was her own labored breath and the splash of a few drops of water falling from her skin. The soak in the tub had relaxed her sore muscles but the warm lethargy coursing through her at that moment had nothing to do with the temperature of her bathwater.

Jackson stared down into her eyes as he pulled the heavy wet cotton from her fingers and dropped it to the floor. He waited several heartbeats, for her to argue she supposed. When she didn't, he slowly drew her to his chest. And, she went to him.

Gina was surprised the contact between them didn't sizzle—her skin, wet and cool, his hot and dry. Jackson's arms angled around her until their skin seemed melded together, shoulders to waist, bare chest to bare breasts. Gina felt more than heard the sound of pleasure that rumbled deep in his chest and experienced a tightening deep inside her. Even as tired as she was, he could still send her senses reeling . . . and leave her wanting. He held her weight against him and for the first time in a week she felt light, not weighed down by her cast, or by the many things she needed to do and couldn't.

She lowered her face to his bare shoulder and breathed in the male smell of him . . . and remembered. One night alone with him. A night of pure pleasure spent in his bed, with his total and undivided attention. A night she was sure she'd never forget. Gina shifted slightly. The sweet friction of his hard chest against her breasts caused her to draw in a quick breath to counteract the quiver of excitement coursing through her. Then she realized that, for all intents and purposes, they were nearly naked and alone right now.

Jackson's hand moved upward until his fingers speared through the hair she'd pinned up to keep dry. He slowly pulled back until she was looking up at him.

The expression on his face made her shiver in his arms. Pain. He looked like a man about to face a firing squad. Need. Like a man who'd stood on the outside for a lifetime watching the warmth and light on the other side of the window.

"Remember what happened New Year's Eve?" he asked as he lowered his jaw to lightly tease her cheek with his short soft whiskers.

Gina's heart pounded in time with his. Words were beyond her limited abilities at that moment. She closed her eyes and let her head fall back, giving him access to her neck.

"I want it to happen again," he said as he nuzzled her damp skin.

Goose bumps rose on her arms and her nipples tightened even more. Gina opened her mouth but no sound came out. Jackson seemed to take that as an invitation because a heartbeat later his lips coaxed her mouth to open wider and his tongue brushed along hers.

"I want it to happen now."

10

JACKSON STEPPED BACKWARD, pulling Gina with him until he was half sitting on the bathroom counter with her practically in his lap. Then he kissed her, deep and wild, as if she were his last meal . . . and he'd been hungry for a long time.

All the blood seemed to drain out of Gina's head and pool like a warm, bubbling spring in her belly. She braced her hands on the cool leather covering his thighs while his fingers kneaded her back then teased her breasts. She wanted his mouth on her breasts . . . she wanted . . .

"Gina . . ." he whispered again, calling to her in his low voice. Her body recognized the sound, the meaning. "Gina, let me love you again." A shudder ran through the muscles of his chest, his arms tightened around her. "Please."

She thought of all the reasons why they shouldn't, why they couldn't, but then he bit her shoulder and jarred her out of any semblance of rational thought. She wanted him, maybe even more than she had on New Year's Eve. Because now she knew his touch, knew what he tasted like, and how he fit inside her. And she was too tired to fight the wonderful feelings that were replacing her fatigue and pain.

"Hand me my robe," she said before she had time to change her mind. As he draped her robe around her, she tried to act casual, as if she'd done this a few times before. When in truth, no man had been in her bed since she'd lost Mike. "You'll have to help me up the stairs." Her voice sounded braver than she felt.

Jackson kissed her one more time, quick and hard, then opened the bathroom door.

The air was a lot cooler outside the steamy closeness of the bathroom. Gina turned her face into Jackson's warm shoulder as he carefully carried her up the stairs. "To the left," she murmured into his skin when they reached the top. Then he was lowering her on to the cool sheets of her own queen-size bed. It felt like a cloud in heaven compared to the trundle bed downstairs.

"Jackson?"

"Yeah?" He paused with his hands on his hips, waiting, as if he expected her to change her mind and ask him to leave.

"Will you do me a favor and check to make sure Emma is asleep . . . and lock the front door?"

Even in the semidarkness she could see his body relax. "Sure."

He returned with something in his hand. Gina couldn't say what because one moment his large silhouette blocked the door, then the door was shut and locked. She rolled closer to the night table and switched on the reading lamp.

Jackson set the bottle he'd been carrying on the nightstand and Gina realized it was her body lotion from the bathroom downstairs. He removed his boots, sat sideways on the edge of the bed facing her, then dropped one arm to cage her close to him.

"Emma is sound asleep, and the house is locked." He leaned forward to kiss her lightly before his hands moved to the edges of her robe. "Now, let's get rid of this." In three swift movements, Gina was naked except for her cast.

Jackson dropped her robe to the floor, studied her bare body for several heart-pounding seconds before he pushed to his feet. Gina had been in the dark with him the first time but now, as she watched him work the fastening of his leather pants, she could feel warmth and color rising to her face. What did someone wear under leather pants? She had no doubt that she was about to find out.

She didn't expect he'd be wearing black briefs that looked like cotton bicycle shorts. They fit his hips and thighs like a second skin and looked comfortable except for the blatant hardness straining at the front. He didn't remove them. He pushed the sheets down to the bottom of the bed before sitting next to her again. Then he picked up the bottle of lotion and twisted off the top.

"This is what I wanted to do in the hospital," he said as he squeezed some lotion into his palm and reached for her hand.

The lotion smelled of raspberries, and as Jackson massaged it over Gina's skin, the sweetness deepened and rose through her senses like a dreamy haze. He rubbed it on her hands, between her fingers, tugging on each one before moving up to the sore muscles in her arms. Gina's blood slowed its reckless pace and for the first time in days she let go and relaxed.

She remembered his touch, but this was different. Sensual but without demand . . . unselfish. He worked the muscles of her uninjured leg, down to her knee, and kissed each toe after he'd smoothed it with his fingers. He rubbed the bottom of her foot with a slow steady stroke until it went beyond tickling and became a twisting heat low in her belly.

He carefully rubbed her right leg above the cast, paying special attention to the soft inner area of her thighs. Her skin warmed to his touch and each time he neared the apex of her thighs she strained upward following his hands.

She didn't resist when he helped her roll over. Her muscles had lost their tenseness and she'd lost any feeling of reluctance. She moaned when he rubbed her back and shoulders. Not in pain...in pleasure. Gina couldn't remember ever feeling as pampered. It made her want to touch him, to make him feel the same.

When he lowered her on her back once more, her arms came up of their own accord and wrapped around his neck. She needed to kiss him, to share the warm lethargy he'd given her.

His mouth was hot and met hers with more urgency than she'd expected. His hands had been unhurried, calm and gentle. There was nothing calm about his kiss or gentle about the hardness she could feel pressed against her hip.

He dragged his mouth from hers. "I haven't done the front yet," he said breathlessly and scooted downward before she could draw him back.

His lotion-slicked hands on her breasts were the final torture. The roughness of his palms on her nipples made her grit her teeth and twist the edge of the pillowcase with restless fingers. But somewhere in the middle of the massage he decided to use his mouth on her nipples instead of his hands.

Jackson felt Gina rise to meet the slow, wet pressure of his tongue and his erection grew harder and more insistent, if that was possible. He loved the way she responded to his touch. He sucked gently, then a bit harder, and her fingers tangled in his hair to keep him close. She was already hot enough to sizzle, but he knew he couldn't take her like he had on New Year's. Not fast and hard like his body demanded. She seemed to have forgotten her broken leg, but he hadn't.

He could take her where she wanted to go, however. With his hands...with his mouth. He escaped from her insistent fingers and slid lower, kissed her belly, then moved lower still.

Gina cried out when he touched her with his tongue. The sound went through him like a gunshot and hardened more than his resolve. She might not have invited him to the party...but she wanted him in her bed. And he could ease that want. He delved deeper, slower, wetter as she twisted beneath him, her response driving him on. She pulled him closer, dug her nails into his shoulder, then suddenly tried to push him away.

"No, please. I want you— I want us ..."

He hesitated for a few heartbeats, but the heat of her, the taste of her was too alluring. He wanted her to come, hard, without fear of repercussions. He wanted her trust again, as she'd trusted him on New Year's before he'd made one stupid mistake.

Jackson lowered his mouth to her once more and the muscles of her thighs bunched in reaction. He felt the sharp tug of her surrender. He slid his hands under her bottom to hold her close. Then she was moaning, arching beneath him. Shuddering under the pressure of his tongue and lips.

Gina fell asleep in his arms, their bodies fitted together like two spoons. It had taken some time for the tenseness to ease out of his system. But she'd fallen right to sleep. As he listened to her even breathing he couldn't resist running a hand over the smooth flat plane of her belly. She stirred slightly at his touch. Was his child growing inside her? Instead of being worried, he realized that if they'd made a baby, it might just be the best thing that had ever happened to him. And he had no idea what to do about it.

JACKSON ROLLED OVER on the couch and opened his eyes. Emma stood a foot away staring at him with open fascination. "You spent the night," she said, stating the obvious. Then she put out one finger and tentatively touched his chin. "Your face is fuzzy."

"Ouch!" he said, pretending that she'd hurt him. She withdrew her hand so fast he laughed. She laughed, too. He pushed up to a sitting position on the couch and rubbed a hand down his face. Then he reached for his watch that he'd left on the coffee table.

"Where's Mommy?"

"She's upstairs in her room," Jackson said as he looked at the time. Eight-fifteen. Too early to be up on a Sunday morning. Emma turned for the door, heading for the stairs.

"Em? Why don't we let her sleep a little longer?"

She stopped and pivoted to look at him. "Can you make bacon?"

Hell, if he could read her books, he could cook. "How hard can it be?" he said and stood, pulling his sweatshirt over his head. He wished he'd worn something besides leather pants. They were great for riding in the cold, but for sleeping they left a lot to be desired. "You go get the bacon out of the refrigerator. I'll meet you there."

Emma made a beeline for the kitchen, dragging her blanket with her. Jackson stepped into the downstairs bathroom and closed the door.

GINA WOKE with a start. She could have sworn she heard the doorbell. Then she realized she was in her own room, her own bed, alone. Had she dreamed the night before with Jackson?

The distant sound of men's voices interrupted her speculation. When she heard the front door close she knew she hadn't been dreaming. The clock near the bed read nine-thirty. She pushed her way out of bed, picked up her robe from the floor and put it on. Then she slowly limped to the top of the stairs.

"Jackson?" She could see his large shoulders because his back was to the stairs, but she couldn't see who he was talking to. At the sound of his name, he turned and Gina saw Nick.

"Mama." Emma clamored up the stairs in her direction. "Uncle Nick is here. And . . ."

"Uncle Vince," a familiar voice added. A voice Gina had known all her life. She stared down at the frown on her brother's face and felt like crawling back into bed and covering her head with the pillows.

Emma reached Gina as she said, "Vince, what are you doing here?"

"Is there a law against visiting my sister?" he asked, glancing toward Jackson as if he might argue.

"N-no . . ." Gina sputtered trying to find her equilibrium. "You just surprised me, that's all. Please, go on in and sit down. Let me get dressed and I'll be there in a few minutes."

"Send Emma to get me when you're ready," Jackson said before turning toward the kitchen.

By the time Gina had washed her face and gotten dressed, she had herself under control. Well, as much control as could be expected given the circumstances. She felt as though the events of the night before were written in great scarlet letters across her forehead for Nick and now Vince to read. She'd forgotten she would have to face Jackson first until he walked into her bed-room.

She'd been sitting on the bed but having him tower over her only made it worse. She pushed up to stand but as she looked into his eyes, she seemed to lose the power of speech.

"Are you okay?" he asked without touching her.

She nodded.

He looked unconvinced. "You sure?" He touched her hair lightly near the bandage covering her stitches.

Gina let out the breath she'd been holding and nodded. "I think so. What did my brother say?"

Jackson's mouth twisted into a hard line. "Hasn't said much of anything. He did ask if that was my motor-cycle parked out front. Emma had already told him I stayed the night."

She stared at him a long time, trying to think of something to diffuse the situation. It would be nice if they could simply meet and be friendly. But she knew Vince, and from what she knew of Jackson, they'd never find any common ground. She caught herself in the middle of her wishful thinking. What did it matter anyway? They didn't have to like each other. It wasn't as if she and Jackson were engaged or anything.

They'd been engaged in something the night before, her conscience reminded her. Memories of his gentle touch and his seductive mouth curled through her, causing her skin to grow warm. Those scarlet letters she'd imagined on her forehead felt as if they were glowing brighter. And Jackson merely watched her, waiting. She had to say something.

"He's always been overprotective," she hedged. "And he's a true New Yorker," she added as if that explained everything.

"Hey, if I'm the problem, I'll leave. I've had my coffee."

"You aren't the problem," Gina said with more certainty than she felt. She'd seen Jackson's bad-boy act. "This is my house and my life." And hopefully Nick could prevent anything physical happening between the two of them.

Jackson looked unconvinced but after a shrug of what looked like indifference, he bent and picked her up. "Let's go see what he has to say."

Gina smelled the scent of coffee and bacon as Jackson carried her down the stairs. At the bottom, instead of walking toward the living room, he made a right into the kitchen. He made his way directly to an empty chair at the kitchen table across from Nick and Vince. Both of them stood as Jackson placed her on her feet. Gina was just beginning to realize exactly how all this looked.

Jackson had made coffee and breakfast for Emma . . . and answered the door in bare feet as if he'd lived in her house for weeks, instead of one night.

"Hey, Sis," Vince said and gave her a quick hug. Then he looked down at her cast. "How're ya doin'?" The familiar sound of his accent, something she'd worked to smooth out of her own speech, made her suddenly teary. She fought the feeling. In the years since she'd moved to Atlanta with Mike, Vince had badgered her constantly about moving back to Buffalo, back to the family. It wouldn't do to show how much she missed them at times.

"I'm doin' good," she answered, mimicking his words. She lowered herself into the chair and glanced at Jackson as he set a cup of coffee in front of her. "I guess you've met Jackson."

Vince remained standing, and for a few heartbeats, he and Jackson stood eye to eye. "Yeah," Vince said. "Sorta."

"Uncle Nick." Emma pulled at Nick's arm. He sat down and she climbed into his lap. "Jackson bought me a dirt bike for my birthday."

"He did?" Nick spoke in a comically surprised voice.

The tension in the room dissipated for a moment, and Vince sat down and faced Emma. "I think I might have something in my suitcase for your birthday from your grandma."

"A present?" Emma perked up. "Where?"

The next several minutes were spent retrieving Emma's present and waiting for her to open it. It was as if all the adults in the room were in tacit agreement not to start something. Jackson left briefly, the creak of the stairs and sound of his movements upstairs made Gina want to talk or sing or tap-dance. Anything to distract her brother and Nick from the truth. In a few moments, Jackson returned wearing his boots, leather jacket and an unreadable expression.

"Look, it's a million brand new crayons" Emma said, holding out her present to show Jackson.

Jackson studied the art set for longer than Gina would have expected him to, then he said, "Cool." His gaze shifted to Gina. "I'm gonna hit the road."

Gina used the arms of the chair to stand. "I'll walk with you—"

"No." An awkward silence followed. Jackson took two steps which brought him within touching distance. Then in front of Emma, her brother Vince and Nick, he kissed her lightly on the mouth and ran the fingers of one hand through her hair. "I'll talk to you later."

He nodded to Nick and Vince then dropped a hand on Emma's head as he moved toward the door. "See ya, shortstuff."

11

"SO, HOW LONG are you staying?" Gina asked her brother.

Nick had left on Jackson's heels and Emma was currently engaged in taking apart her new art set in the playroom.

"As long as it takes to get you to go back with me," Vince answered.

Gina couldn't tell by his tone how serious he might be. He'd never been shy about making demands.

"You know Ma wants to see you, and now that you're not able to work, why not?" He shrugged as if he'd already convinced her.

"I can't take off just like that. Emma is in school, I've got doctors appointments, and . . . commitments."

"I see," Vince said, sitting back in his chair and leveling his inquisitor gaze at her. "So, who is this guy?"

Gina hadn't been talking about Jackson particularly when she'd mentioned commitments, but for the last week she'd been unsuccessful at evicting him from her thoughts for very long. She couldn't just up and leave with everything between them so unsettled. She'd learned as a cop that loose ends would come back to haunt you.

"He's a friend," Gina hedged. "Nick knows him."

"Funny, Nick never mentioned him when I asked about you. And, in Buffalo anyway, someone who spends the night is a little more than a friend."

"Maybe Nick knows I don't like you keeping tabs on me," Gina snapped. "I'm all grown up, Vinny."

"You're still my baby sister. Look, I know you've had a tough time with what happened to Mike and all. Now with this accident— You should be closer to your family, closer to people who would look out for you and Emma."

"I have plenty of help. I have Nick, my friend Vickie, and Jackson." At least, she thought, she'd have Jackson until they found out if she was pregnant or not.

"Jackson." Vince made a sound of disgust. "What kind of name is that, anyway?"

Gina had to laugh at her brother's natural prejudice for anything that wasn't Northern Italian Catholic. "It's a distinguished *Southern* name."

"Distinguished, yeah, right," he said, unconvinced. "Do leather pants and a motorcycle make him more distinguished?"

"Look, Vinny, Jackson isn't the issue here—"

"Well, he should be. What about Emma? What does she think about all this?"

"Emma is crazy about Jackson—"

"Are you gonna marry the guy? What do you know about him?" Vince interrupted, ready for an argument.

His attitude made Gina bristle even though she'd had the same thoughts earlier. "Nobody's talking about marriage here. We're just—" *Just what?* her mind questioned, *playing around?* If she'd ever met anyone in her life less likely to be playing, it was Jackson. If he'd been merely playing New Year's Eve, he certainly wouldn't have stuck around to know the outcome.

Vinny looked disgusted. "You're a cop, for cryin' out loud. I can't believe you're this naive."

"What are you talking about?"

"Are this guy's intentions honorable? It looks like he's using Emma to get to you. Have you thought of that? He's buying her bicycles and—"

"He's *not* using Emma."

"How do you know?"

She realized her brother was playing his usual role of devil's advocate, but the question was valid. *How did she know?* Because of the way Jackson touched her, kissed her. She could feel the hunger in him. Besides, Emma had run to Jackson, not the other way around. Most of the time, he seemed surprised by her adoration.

Still, Jackson had admitted to giving up his daughter. He had lost a child. Could that be part of his interest in Emma? Did he want to replace the child he'd given up by being around Emma? Or would he leave Emma behind as well?

"Who put you in charge of my life?" she asked, falling back into her familiar sister-brother routine. "You haven't been here two hours and you're already making me crazy."

He smiled at that. "It's my mission in life."

"Great," Gina sighed and wondered how her life could get turned so completely upside down in so short a time. Well, on New Year's Eve she'd said she wanted to start again. She just hadn't realized that change would be this confusing. She shifted her leg to a more comfortable position and began a mental list of decisions she needed to make.

JACKSON SIGNED the check and gave it to Tyler.

"This is too much money," Tyler said and handed it back.

"Take it," Jackson ordered, refusing to accept it. "Buy Steve some new scarves for his act."

Tyler frowned. "This would buy a lot of scarves. What's up with you?"

Jackson turned away and busied himself by putting away his checkbook. He knew he'd felt unsettled but he hadn't realized other people might notice. "What do you mean?"

"You're acting weird," Tyler persisted.

"Now there's a statement, coming from someone like you." Jackson flinched at his own words. There it was again, *someone like you*. He'd never thought he'd use that tone with anyone, having faced it all his adult life.

"Don't try to make me mad. I'm being serious here," Tyler went on, unfazed.

Jackson had to hand it to him. Tyler was who he was and if someone didn't like it, then they had no taste. "I'm sorry—" he began to say but the shock on Tyler's face stopped him.

"I think I need to sit down," he said dramatically. "Jackson Gray is apologizing?"

"Very funny," Jackson said.

The humor left Tyler. "What's wrong? You're not sick, are you?" Then he looked even more troubled. "My God, you haven't decided that you're gay, have you?"

Jackson almost choked. "No, nothing like that. I'm just— It's about Gina."

"Oh." Tyler looked relieved. "You mean you've finally figured out that you've fallen in love?"

I'M *NOT IN LOVE*, Jackson repeated to himself as he dialed the telephone. He'd waited twenty-four hours and he just wanted to hear Gina's voice, to make sure she was all right. He wasn't in love.

A man answered the phone. "Hello?"

Jackson recognized the voice and the accent of the disapproving brother. All of his defenses went into overdrive. "Is Gina there?"

"Yeah, she's here. Who's this?"

"Jackson Gray," he said without emotion. He wasn't going to give the guy the satisfaction of making him mad.

"You know, it's hard for her to get to the phone with her cast—"

Jackson heard Gina's voice in the background but he couldn't make out the words.

"Hold on," the brother said.

"Hello?" Gina said a short time later.

Everything inside Jackson that had been tense eased at hearing her voice. "Hey," he said. "I wanted to check on you, see how you're doing."

"I'm doing much better today. I'm not so tired." She sounded formal, careful and Jackson knew that her brother must be sitting and listening to the conversation.

"Well, that's good." Now that he had the formalities out of the way, he had no idea how to keep the conversation going. So, he asked for what he wanted. "I thought I might stop by tomorrow night. Maybe take you and Emma out for pizza." He'd wanted to see Gina alone, to really talk, but it didn't seem right leaving Emma out.

"Um. You know my brother is here. And, I'm not really supposed to be walking around on this cast."

Jackson gave it one last shot. "I could bring the pizza there."

Gina hesitated and he thought she might say yes. But she didn't. "I don't think we'd be much fun. Maybe another time."

He wanted to say, "Who's we?" but he held his temper. He could accept it if she really didn't want to be with him, but he'd seen her brother's reaction to his presence in Gina's house. He had the distinct feeling that Vince was the one who didn't want to see him. And Gina was going along with him.

He let it go. "Okay, some other time then."

"I go back to the doctor on Thursday for my walking cast," Gina said. "By the way, do you have Tyler's phone number? I can't find it. He was supposed to give me a total of the expenses for Emma's party."

Still smarting from Gina's reluctance to allow him into her life, Jackson forgot to be careful. "I've already paid him," he said.

"What? Well, how much was it? I'll send you a check."

Jackson could hear the change in her voice, shifting from friendly to businesslike and that made him even madder. "Forget it," he said.

He heard her draw in a breath in the ensuing silence. "Jackson," she said stiffly. "I can't let you pay for Emma's party."

Jackson was past being cooperative. "Why not? I wanted to pay for it. It was my idea."

"Can't you see how that looks?" she asked finally.

"How it looks? I wanted Emma to have a party, so I paid for one. It's only money, and I told you I can afford it. Why should I care how it looks?"

"Because I care."

She was right. He knew she was right but somehow he'd hoped— "I understand. I'll give you a total next time we talk."

"Thank you." The relieved sound in her voice made him feel like swearing.

"Gina?"

"Uh-huh?"

"Don't say anything for a minute, just listen, okay?" He had to get this out without thinking about what Vince might be overhearing.

"Okay."

Jackson tightened his grip on the phone and said what he had to say. "I know things are a little crazy for you right now, and I'm part of it. And I don't intend to make things worse, but I want to see you. I think you know that."

"I—"

"Just listen," Jackson repeated and leaned his forehead against the wall near the phone. He had to make it her choice, but the hell of it was, she might not choose what he hoped she would. "You have my number, and you know where I am." He swallowed to ease the unfamiliar dryness in his throat. "If you want to see me, let me know. All right?"

"Yes . . . I will."

JACKSON POPPED the igniter for the welding torch and shoved the heavy hood down to shield his eyes. The last three days he'd cut enough metal to build two bridges, or at least it felt that way. Jerry, his helper, had nearly mutinied. Now, he was several hours into the morning of the third day and Gina still hadn't called.

He'd given her the choice so he'd just have to wait, but it had been a long time since he'd waited for anything. His only option was to work. He couldn't storm over to Gina's house and confront her. He wished he knew a way to make her understand what he was feeling. To make her want to see him. To make her call.

He'd once dated a woman who professed to be a witch. She'd been full of information and so-called spells to attract a job or money or love. At the time, he'd had all the jobs and money he needed, and he wasn't interested in love. Now he wished he'd paid more attention.

How the hell had he gotten himself into this mess? He knew better. He wasn't in love. He had rules—not to hurt anyone and not to let anyone hurt him.

The ringing of the front bell and the corresponding flashing light over his workbench interrupted his thoughts.

"I'll go," Jerry called over the noise of the torch. Jackson's smile was hidden by the mask. Jerry would do anything for a break.

As the door to Jackson's loft opened, Gina did her best to smile. But, her smile faded when she saw that it wasn't Jackson who'd answered the door.

"Hi. Is Jackson here?" she said a little too brightly for her own peace of mind. Why was she so nervous? Jackson wanted to hear what she had to tell him.

"Yeah," the man said, then glanced down at her brand-new walking cast. He stepped back to give her room to get through the door. "He's in the studio. I can take you back, or go get him."

Her natural curiosity shifted into high gear. She wanted to see where he worked. "I can walk pretty well now," she said as she crossed the threshold. In the warmth of the living room, she started to slip off her coat.

"You might want to keep that on," the man said. "It's pretty cool in the back. Follow me."

He adjusted to her slower gait as they walked past the living room. The man guiding her walked right by the doorway that Gina knew was Jackson's bedroom then paused to open an etched metal door decorated in the design of a giant spider web. Gina's first view of Jackson was of his back amid a shower of sparks. The man who had answered the door motioned to her to stop when they were about ten feet away.

"Jackson!" he shouted.

The sparks stopped and Jackson pushed the hood up as he turned. She could only stare at him for a long moment. His hands were covered by heavy leather gloves but he was dressed in a worn T-shirt, jeans and heavy black work boots. A leather apron covered his chest. His face was grimy with soot from the flame but his eyes had never looked bluer.

The welding torch popped as he switched it off. "Hey," he said sounding wary. Slowly and carefully he pulled the hood off and then the gloves, never taking his eyes off her.

Gina's pulse pounded in her throat and she swallowed to ease the flutter. She'd wanted to see him but she'd forgotten just how overwhelming he could be. She searched for words so she wouldn't make a fool out of herself in the first two minutes.

When nothing appropriate occurred to her, she purposefully pulled her gaze from his and glanced around his workshop stalling for time. The space was the size of a basketball court, filled with unfamiliar tools, and in one corner stood something that looked like a furnace.

"This looks like Dr. Frankenstein's lab," she joked.

Jackson set the gloves and mask aside and crossed his arms. "I suppose you could say we've built a few monsters in here. None of them are walking around though." He cocked his head toward the man standing near her. "You met Jerry?"

Gina nodded. "Hi, I'm Gina." He returned her greeting.

"Jerry, why don't you take a break and run over to the store to pick up the snips and bits I ordered?"

"Sure thing," Jerry answered.

Jackson watched her in silence until Jerry left the room. When they were alone he said, "It's good to see you." The hard expression on his face gave no indication of his mood. His gaze shifted to her new cast. "How's the leg?"

"Better." She turned her leg as if to model for him. "Just got the new walking cast this morning. I'm slow, but I'm mobile."

He moved forward and uncrossed his arms as if he might touch her, but stopped. "Let's go up front where it's warmer," he said. "I need to wash up."

He walked her back to the front of the building, then seated her at the counter dividing the kitchen from the living area. Gina used the opportunity to study Jackson's home. She hadn't taken the time, or had the inclination when she'd been there New Year's Day. She'd been too upset. There was no reason to be upset now. She had the answer to the question they'd argued about.

Looking around, she realized again how little she really knew about his life, when he'd made it his business to find out about hers. He'd shown up at the precinct, the hospital and her house.

The furniture filling his living room was sleek and sophisticated, artistic but masculine. Leather and metal counterbalanced here and there with small colorful pieces of art, such as the Japanese calligraphy in neon and the blown glass bowl sitting in the center of an end table the color of copper.

A grown-up place, not like her home which was scattered with toys and the aftermath of whatever Emma had taken apart or locked together on any given day. The room before her held no evidence of his connection to the people in his life. No pictures, obvious gifts or feminine touches. If there had been a woman in

Jackson's life in the recent past, her presence didn't show.

"I feel a little more human now," Jackson said as he walked toward her. His hair was wet and the streaks of soot were gone from his skin. He'd also changed shirts. But he hadn't shaved and the roughness of his jaw made him look dangerous. "Now I can do what I wanted to do before." With that he leaned close, cupped her cheek with his palm and gave her a light kiss on the opposite cheek before moving in for a more leisurely one on her mouth. Then, he backed off. "I probably still smell like a rhinoceros though."

The prickling of his slight beard against her skin sent Gina's nerve endings into overload. She smiled in spite of her body's helpless reaction to his overpowering nearness. He smelled just fine to her. "Been hanging around at the zoo again?"

A brief wicked grin transformed his features. "I've been meaning to tell you—I'm a little kinky."

His uncharacteristic playfulness sent a current of warmth through her. If he ever took up smiling full-time, she'd be in serious trouble. "Nobody is that kinky," Gina quipped but the oblique reference to what she did and didn't know about him brought her back to her reason for being there. There was one thing she knew for certain as of this morning—Jackson hadn't made a baby with her. She had to stop stalling. He had a right to hear the news and the fact that she had mixed feelings didn't count for much.

"Jackson, I . . ."

He seemed to sense the change of mood and his whole body went still.

"I'm not pregnant." There, she'd said it. She couldn't see any change or relief in him. He stared at her without speaking. "I . . . um. I started my period this morning. Everything seems normal."

A flicker of something flashed in his eyes before he looked away. "So—" he crossed his arms then brought his gaze back to hers "—how do you feel about that?"

"Great," she managed to reply but inwardly winced at the lie. She didn't feel great. Relieved, maybe, but not great. "My life has been so wild for the last few weeks, I certainly didn't need something else to handle right now. And you—"

"I would have helped you handle it," he said simply.

Gina watched him for any signs of squirming, but he was steady as a rock. "I believe you would have," she said after a moment.

"What happens now?" he asked, speaking aloud the question that was blaring in her mind. What was she supposed to say? *It's been fun but—*

"What do you mean?" she asked, stalling.

"Between us."

Now it was Gina's turn to squirm, and by the look on his face he wasn't going to make it easy. Her logic screamed the facts: they were too different and had nothing in common. They didn't even know each other that well. She knew, without a doubt, she could search this place from top to bottom without ever finding that white picket fence she wanted. But her heart remembered his rare smiles, his concern, and the way her daughter trusted him. Her body remembered everything about his touch. She ran a hand over her face and sighed. "I don't know."

"What do you want to happen?"

The corner she'd backed into began to shrink around her. "There have been several things in my life that I've wanted. Having them didn't always make me happy."

Jackson uncrossed his arms before pulling out the chair next to hers. He sat down and leaned toward her bracing his forearms on his knees. His blue gaze held her prisoner. "What do you want?"

"What do I want from you? Or from my life?"

"Both."

She skipped over the first and went for the second. If he wanted to know then she'd tell him. "I want the house with the white picket fence. You're looking at a temporarily out of work, single mother who has a dangerous job and a daughter to raise. I want what other people have—a whole family. A husband and a father for Emma, a home. Something and someone to depend on."

Gina put one of her hands on Jackson's. "You have your life just like you want it. Your work—" she raised the other hand and gestured to the room "—this place. Everything. No matter how attracted I am to you—"

"Wait." He stopped her by squeezing her hand between his. "Stop there for a second.

"First of all, you're right about me. I do live as I please and have for years. I stopped opening up and letting people pick me apart a long time ago. But I care about you." He tugged on her fingers in an almost nervous gesture. "Why don't we start over and see how it turns out?"

The word *yes* leaped into her mind but she didn't say it. That would be asking for trouble. She could have him, but not the life she wanted. If they said goodbye now, there would be no connection, no consequences. If they started over and her feelings, which were already stronger than she'd expected, grew stronger . . .

"I'm not sure that's a good idea," she said. "I have Emma to think about. She's already attached to you." *And so am I.*

"Is that so bad?" he questioned with a puzzled frown. "I sort of like it."

Gina looked him in the eyes. "It's only bad when you leave and I have to try to explain why."

"I'm not going anywhere."

"That's my point. You have what you want. I made a resolution New Year's Eve to get what I want. To find a normal, nice guy to help me put together a whole family and a home." She inclined her head toward the room. "This isn't it. And you are who you are. Do you understand what I'm saying?"

He released her hand and framed her face. His fingers pushed into her hair as he drew her closer. "Yes I do. I can be nice but I've never claimed to be normal. What about us, though? You and me?" The hard line of his jaw softened, his gaze heated and shifted from questioning to caressing. Then his mouth was on hers, touching, teasing. "What about how we make each other feel?" he asked in between kisses designed to remind and convince.

A jolt ran through Gina sending her pulse into fast forward. He wasn't playing fair and they both knew it. But she didn't pull away, from the kiss or the question. "If it was just about you and me—"

"It is about you and me," he said close to her ear.

She shook her head and leaned back to look in his eyes. He didn't get it. He didn't see how complicated her life was, how being a mother changed things. How closing yourself off to the world wouldn't work when you had a family. She'd come here to tell him that they weren't forever linked by a child they'd made. This was the perfect place to break off their brief connection. Before one of them got hurt.

"I'm a cop, Jackson. I learned a long time ago about dealing with reality. I also learned to size up a situation for potential problems. . . . If you look at how different we are—"

"Are you psychic, too?" he asked with an amused twist of his mouth. "Can you predict the outcome of every dangerous situation?" His expression went from charming to serious in the space of a breath. "I want you— I care about you, that's reality. And you want me." His fingers moved downward to her neck and stopped. "At least from here down. It's a start."

12

JACKSON RELEASED her and backed off, as if he'd made his case. "How did you get here?" he asked. The 180 degree turn in the conversation couldn't have been more obvious if he'd said, *How about this weather we're having?*

It took Gina a moment to gather her scattered defenses. The instant he'd touched her, kissed her, her body had turned traitor and she was having a difficult time sticking to her game plan.

"Vince drove me. He's over at T.J.'s." Probably pacing the floor, she thought. "She and Nick have invited Vince, Emma and I to dinner tonight at her place."

"Good old Vince," Jackson said without any particular inflection. He crossed his arms and went silent.

"T.J. said to ask you, too," Gina continued. It was true, T.J. had made the offer, but until this moment, Gina hadn't intended to extend the invitation. After running all the possible sources of disaster through her mind as she'd crossed the courtyard, she'd decided that sitting through a meal with her brother and Jackson at the same table would be hazardous to her mental health—not to mention her digestion.

Jackson uncrossed his arms. "Yeah, I can do that. What time?"

Gina had to work to hide her feeling of dread. Her brother could be relentless and he thought he had the perfect right to butt into her life. He'd do his best to aggravate Jackson. In the middle of reciting her recipe for disaster, realization struck. This was the perfect way for Jackson to understand how family worked—for better or for worse. Time for a dose of reality, for both of them.

"We have to pick up Emma, then go home and get changed. We'll be there at six-thirty," she answered, managing a slight smile. "But I have to warn you, my brother is a hard case when it comes to me and Emma."

"I'm not worried. I'll be there."

AT EXACTLY six-thirty, T.J.'s doorbell rang. Emma beat Gina to the door.

"Jackson!" Emma managed to sound surprised and delighted at the same time. Gina was experiencing those same feelings herself.

He was dressed in black again, the same jeans and sweater he'd worn New Year's Eve, and he'd shaved. The subtle reminder of all that had happened between them that night sent a swirl of heat through her.

"Hey, Emma," he said, ruffling her hair with one hand. The fingers of his other hand were wrapped around the business end of two bottles of wine.

Gina had chosen her own clothes very carefully for the occasion. Jackson had never seen her decked out in anything other than her uniform and a motley assortment of clothes worn to accommodate her cast. She wanted to hide the cast yet feel dressed up for the occasion, so she'd worn the ankle-length, royal blue velvet skirt and matching vest that had been hanging in her closet for two years since the mayor's election celebration.

Jackson paused to look at her from head to toe but Emma was already pulling at his hand, dragging him inside. With a smile he let her, stopping briefly near Gina.

"You look terrific," he whispered. Then he kissed her high, closer to her ear than to her mouth and in the process slid the smooth shaven warmth of his jaw along hers. The sensation echoed through Gina's skin and raised gooseflesh on her neck. To anyone else it must have looked like an innocent hello kiss. Gina knew different.

His earlier words drifted back to her. *What about how we make each other feel?* It appeared as though he intended to use her physical reaction to him alternately as a carrot and a club. The club part had just struck her squarely between the eyes.

The evening started out with a bang. As Jackson placed the bottles of wine on the counter in order to greet T.J., Vince and Nick, Vince set the tone.

He twirled one of the bottles of wine and read the label, then nodded in appreciation. "Hey, this is good stuff. I figured you'd bring a bottle of Jack Daniels. Isn't that what *you all* drink down here in the South?"

Jackson faced him squarely, and Gina held her breath. "I have some over at my place if you want to try it," he answered. It sounded more like a threat than an offer.

"Vince," Gina warned. "Cut it out."

"Jackson?" Emma chimed in. When he looked down at her she asked, "Will you play Go Fish with me?"

"Sure," he responded.

"Yes, why don't we all play?" Gina added quickly. "You, me and Jackson. T.J. won't let me help in the kitchen." As she followed Emma and Jackson out of the kitchen area, Vince gave her a last-of-the-traitors frown. She shrugged it off. She wanted to say, *you deserve it,* but held her tongue. "Why don't you open the wine, Vinny?" she asked sweetly instead.

DINNER WAS GOING BETTER than he'd expected, Jackson decided, and mainly because of the women in the room. Especially Emma. If she hadn't been there, he had no doubt that the mood would have degenerated—in a hurry.

He still didn't get it. What had he done to Gina's brother to make him so uptight? Vince seemed determined to draw him out, and not because he wanted to get better acquainted.

Most of the conversation during the meal had been between Nick and Vince concerning the pros and cons of living in Buffalo or Atlanta. Jackson hadn't felt compelled to defend his hometown because Nick had taken up the cause. That is, until Vince began making his case directly to Gina.

"You know, Buffalo is a great place to raise kids," Vince said with his gaze on Emma. "A family kind of place, with neighborhood schools and—"

"I grew up there, Vinny. I know what it's like," Gina answered. "And, it's cold."

"You know, we have neighborhoods here," Jackson said, unable to keep quiet any longer. "We call it the suburbs. And, we rarely get snow."

"This is still a big city, with big-city problems," Vince continued.

"And Buffalo is a smaller city with big-city problems," Gina said. "You can't get away from crime and drugs anymore. It's everywhere."

"Well, at least in Buffalo we know who the crooks and creeps are—"

"My grandma lives in Buffalo and she's not a crook," Emma said.

Vince pounced on the opening. "Wouldn't you like to go and visit your grandma, Emma?"

"Will you stop it?" Gina asked her brother. "That's not fair."

"Can we go, Mommy?"

Gina scowled at Vince before answering. "We'll see, Em. Right now we're just talking."

AROUND EIGHT-THIRTY, Emma started to conk out. They'd played cards, she'd colored in her coloring books, but her sleepy eyes seemed to have a mind of their own and kept closing. Since Gina couldn't navigate the stairs, T.J. offered to read to Emma and took her up to her sleeping loft so the rest of them could talk.

Jackson didn't want to talk. He poured himself another glass of wine then sat on the couch next to Gina. That put him directly across from Vince and Nick who were sitting in chairs on the other side of the coffee table. He figured he could stand Gina's brother for a while longer, as long as he could be close to Gina.

"What do you do for a living?" Vince asked.

"He builds things," Gina answered, making an obvious effort to head him off at the pass.

Vince's gaze never wavered from Jackson's. "What kind of things?"

Jackson's first impulse was to say "none of your business." He'd quit answering questions or justifying himself when he'd left his father's house at sixteen. But he could understand the man's concern for Gina. He'd give him that much. And, Gina had warned him.

"I work with metal," Jackson answered.

"Actually, he's an industrial artist," Nick injected.

Jackson shifted his attention to Nick, wondering how he'd come up with that particular phrasing, and trying to figure out if Nick was helping or hurting his case. He couldn't tell.

"What's that?" Vince continued in a relentless sort of way.

"I build things out of metal—bridges, atrium installations, fountains. It's considered a kind of art."

"Who do you work for?"

The strained thread of Jackson's patience began to fray. "Myself. Want to see my tax returns?"

"Vince, I've changed my mind about the wine. Would you please pour me a glass?" Gina asked.

"In a minute, Sis," he answered.

Jackson picked up his full glass from the end table and handed it to her. "Here, take mine."

Vince stood and reached into the pocket of his jacket. "I know artists don't make much money and it looks like you've invested yours into that motorcycle you ride." He flipped open his checkbook. "I want to pay you for Emma's birthday party."

"That's enough, Vince. I mean it," Gina warned.

"What?" he answered and shrugged at her. "It's only right. Do you even know this guy? He shouldn't be paying for parties and buying bicycles for your daughter."

Jackson pushed to his feet. "I can afford it," he said in a tight voice. In his mind, it seemed too much like history repeating itself, having his motives—and his character—questioned. He would have thought after all these years that he could handle things better this time. But he knew if Gina hadn't been there he would have shoved Mister Buffalo Is The Greatest Place On Earth up against the wall.

"How?" Vinny asked. "You live in this place and you work sometimes—"

"He owns this place," Nick interrupted. "The whole complex, lock, stock and courtyard. It's listed in the real estate holdings of a corporation called—"

"Stop it!" Gina ordered. But she could see it was too late. Jackson had gone utterly still and when he looked at her, his gaze was icy.

"You were right," he said and Gina felt her heart tighten painfully. "If this is what it takes to be normal, then I can't do it."

"Jackson—"

He held up a hand to stop her. "I'm sorry," he said, pulling his gaze away as if looking at her hurt. He faced Vince first. "Keep your money. You got what you wanted." Then he stepped around the coffee table and stopped in front of Nick. "Don't tell Tyler or anyone else what you know about me, or I'll shut this place down in a heartbeat and put everybody on the street. Got it?"

Nick nodded. "Listen, Jackson—"

"Don't," he repeated and walked out.

GINA MADE IT to T.J.'s front windows in time to see light stream out of Jackson's loft door as he opened it. Then the light disappeared as he slammed it shut. She felt as if he'd ripped out her heart and taken it with him. Tears filled her eyes. He'd seemed so alone in the middle of them, surrounded, as if he were on trial and they were the jury. And she hadn't defended him. She hadn't known what to say.

"Gina?" Vince's voice came from behind her.

"Don't talk to me right now, Vinny. Just go away."

"I only want what's best for you and Emma."

She turned to face him. "And what makes you think you know what that is?" she asked, losing the battle with her tears. "Is your life so perfect that you should make everyone else's decisions for them?"

"You know I—"

"I want to go home. And, after you drive us home I want you to stay at Nick's tonight. I don't want to see you or talk to you . . . tonight." She turned and faced Jackson's closed door. "Let me know when you're ready to leave."

SHE HADN'T BEEN HOME thirty minutes before her mother called. With a sigh, Gina gripped the phone tighter and tried to keep her voice from wobbling.

"Hi, mom. Yeah, I'm doing okay." It was a polite lie, but her mother didn't argue. Gina knew Vince must have called and told her what happened.

"I wish you'd let Vince bring you up here for a visit. It seems like such a long time since I've seen you and Emma. And now that you're off from work it would be the perfect time. Emma could bring her schoolwork with her and you could see everyone."

Gina sighed. Sometimes it felt as if her whole family were taking sides against her. And that kind of pressure was hard to fight.

"If money is a problem, you know I'll be glad to pay for the tickets," her mother continued.

"I know, Mom, and thanks. I've just been so busy, there a million things I need to take care of here." Unfinished business. The most important piece being Jackson. She needed to talk to him, to tell him... What? Goodbye? The memory of his face before he'd turned and walked out of T.J.'s made Gina feel hollow inside. Running away wouldn't help. "I don't see how I can do it right now," she said, hoping her mother wouldn't press the issue further.

"Well, if you change your mind, call me."

"I will. I'll talk with you soon. Good night."

Gina hung up the receiver and ran a hand through her hair. She stared at the phone and tried to think of what she was going to say to Jackson. *I'm sorry my brother is such a bully. I'm sorry that my life is so complicated. I wish things could be different. I miss you.*

She did miss him. He'd stepped into her life on New Year's Eve and changed something in her. Now it looked as though he were stepping back out, and she wasn't sure what to do with the new feelings running around inside her.

JACKSON TOSSED the second duffel bag into the back of his van and slammed the door. Time to get out. He hated to admit it, but Gina was right. Nick was right. And, even the inimitable Vince was right. Jackson had no business thinking he could be anything other than a loner, a renegade.

For the last few weeks he'd been fooling himself because he'd wanted Gina. The idea that they might have made a baby New Year's Eve had derailed his normal enthusiasm for a life of independence. Being around Gina and Emma had made him want all sorts of things he'd never thought of before. But wanting didn't mean having.

The expression on Gina's brother's face had told him that in no uncertain terms. Vince and Nick had poked around in his life and cornered him as if he were some kind of sleazebag criminal. Just because he didn't dress and act like them. And Gina hadn't said a word—like Lauren. Lauren had been a scared kid, easily influenced by her parents. Gina was a grown woman who'd warned him about her family, but in the end she'd let him go, too.

Well, he knew how to be the outsider. He'd learned to hide his true feelings from his father behind a smoke screen of attitude and then used that same skill when he'd faced Lauren's family. No one cared enough to dig deeper and find out how he really felt. How many times did he have to have his nose rubbed in it?

He needed to get out of town, to get far enough away from Gina to forget the way she tasted, the way she felt in his arms. And he needed to leave tonight before he did something crazy like drive out to the suburbs and punch her brother. That would certainly endear him to the family—and prove their point.

Jackson walked back to his building, pulled the door shut and locked the dead bolt. Instead of leaving a note, he cut across the dark courtyard and took the stairs up to Tyler's loft two at a time.

GINA LET THE PHONE RING fifteen times before she finally hung up. Where was Jackson? Was he sitting there ignoring the phone or had he taken off on his motorcycle? She limped over to the window and pushed aside the curtain. She'd rather be ignored than think of him on the road in the cold. Alone again.

She jumped when her phone rang. As she limped to answer it she glanced at the clock. Eleven-thirty. If

Vince was calling to apologize again she had a few more things to—

"Hello?"

"What did you do to Jackson?" Tyler's voice sounded distraught and not the least bit friendly.

Gina slowly lowered herself to the couch. "What do you mean?"

"I mean he's gone. He took off and it doesn't look like he's ever coming back. What did you do?" he demanded.

She didn't need to ask why Tyler thought she'd done something. Maybe this outcome had been obvious to everyone from the start. Everyone but Jackson. "Several things he didn't deserve," Gina confessed, fighting the tightness in her throat. "What did he say?"

"Nothing. That's the problem. He just said he's taking a road trip and might not be back for a while." Tyler paused then added, "If you could have seen the look on his face . . ."

Gina blinked and felt hot tears roll down her face. "I'm sorry, Tyler. I've tried to call him."

"You don't understand," Tyler said stiffly. "He left me the keys to his studio, and to the motorcycle. He said if he decided not to come back, he wanted me to sell everything."

Gina sniffed and wiped one cheek with the back of her hand. Even her car accident hadn't hurt this bad. Jackson was gone and it was her fault. "I'm so sorry."

"WELL, HERE WE ARE," Vince said as he pulled his car away from the airport curb. "Beautiful Buffalo, New York."

Beautiful Buffalo. Gina stared out the window at the snow piled along the roadway and shook her head. "I don't know how you think I can get around in the snow with this cast," Gina said. "If I fall and break my other leg, you'll have to support me for life."

As Vince's wife quizzed Emma about the flight, Gina sat back and sighed. Coming home always brought up old memories of Mike and the life that had seemed perfect for a while. And being in Buffalo also meant she had to deal with her family. Her entire family, not just Vince. Since she was the only sibling not settled in Buffalo with a mate and busy having more babies, her life was always up for review. She'd decided to make an appearance to assure everyone she and Emma were fine.

But, she wasn't fine. Jackson was gone. Staying in Atlanta or coming to Buffalo wouldn't change that. It had been five days since she'd seen him. To Gina it felt like fifty.

She'd checked with T.J. and Tyler several times before leaving, but no one had heard from him. Knowing that they were all wrong for each other was one thing. Living without him in her life was turning out to be quite another. The sadness inside her felt suspiciously like grief and she'd grieved for Mike enough to recognize the sensation.

But, she hadn't been in love with Jackson, had she? They'd certainly been in lust. Gina closed her eyes, casting back through her mind to the way he'd melted her defenses. To the spontaneous heat that seemed to flare between them with only a touch or a kiss. To the sound of his low voice whispering her name. *Gina* . . .

Then, without permission, her mind projected a snapshot memory of Jackson holding Emma in his arms after she'd almost crashed on her new bike. Swallowing to fight the itch of tears, Gina opened her eyes. Whether she loved him or not at this moment in time was irrelevant. She couldn't have him.

"Here we are," Vince said as he turned into the driveway to her mother's house. Before the car stopped, the front door opened and Gina's brothers and their wives along with several children came down the front steps.

As Gina pushed open the door on her side of the car, she heard someone say, "Welcome home."

13

JACKSON HAD CHOPPED and hauled wood until his hands were blistered and his shoulders stiff. He rubbed a sore palm over his face and surveyed the neatly stacked pile. He'd have to stay in the cabin all winter to use that much wood.

And he was already going squirrely with cabin fever.

Damn.

He used to love coming here. This cabin in the north Georgia mountains was the one place he and his father had shared without question, without argument. As if it were sacred ground. The neighbors around the Mountaintown Creek area had always treated him with tolerance as they would their own sons, because they knew and respected his father. Jackson had decided early on not to abuse that respect—so every trip he'd left his attitude at the perimeter freeway circling Atlanta. Which was probably why his father had left the land and the cabin to him when he died.

Jackson used one last downward stroke of the ax to embed it into the splitting stump then sat down. This place had always been his refuge—until now.

Damn.

Gina . . . Where was she? How were she and Emma doing without him? *Probably just fine,* his anger answered. As long as they had "dear Uncle Vince" to hover over them. But what was supposed to happen when Uncle Vince went back to his own life? He couldn't look out for them forever . . . unless he talked Gina into moving back to Buffalo.

Jackson had thought coming here would help relieve the pain, hoping that mere distance would take the edge off. But solitude and the surrounding natural beauty had only given him more time to think. He knew now that even if Gina did move back to Buffalo, the added distance wouldn't put a dent in how he felt here in Georgia without her.

"Well, Pop," he said, looking up toward the bare branches overhead. "I've turned out just like you said I would." Except for the money, he thought. Neither of them could have foreseen his success with metalwork. But Jackson was alone, and pretty ticked off about it right at the moment. And that's exactly where his father had said he'd end up. *And you won't be happy about it, even if you think that's what you want now.*

When Jackson had been dealing with Lauren's pregnancy and her holier-than-thou relatives, his own father had told him to fight for his child. Not to give her up because he'd regret it someday.

Someday had hit him right about the time Gina and Emma turned up at the Coach Works. He'd seen first-hand the love he'd missed. And now he knew he'd never be the same.

So what was he supposed to do? Should he do what he'd told Tyler he intended? Repack the van and just hit the road, when the only place he wanted to be was back in Atlanta?

He looked around the familiar surroundings, the weathered cabin he and his father had built together and tried to imagine what his father might say to him now. The answer came, fast and sure.

He couldn't go back and change the past. He'd accepted his loss, long ago. He'd been assured his own daughter was happy and in a stable home. If he tried to be a part of her life now, it would be for him, not his daughter. Maybe someday when she was older... But, Gina and Emma were on their own in the present. They were alone, just like him. And he could do something about that.

Jackson pushed to his feet, stepped up onto the porch, stomped his boots on the mat then went inside the cabin. He picked up his cellular phone and dialed Tyler's number.

Jackson had decided to fight.

"GINA? The phone's for you," her mother called.

Gina put down the half-peeled potato she'd been working on and wiped her hands on a towel before walking into the living room to accept the receiver from her mother. "Hello?"

"Gina?"

She was surprised to hear Nick's voice. "Nick?" He didn't speak right away, as if searching for words. Gina began to worry. "What's going on?"

"I want you to sit down. I have something to tell you."

Gina's heart took several panicked beats. Emma was here and safe, her family was all fine. She looked around and found the closest place to sit—the arm of the couch. "Is it about Jackson?" she asked. "Has something happened to him?"

"No," Nick said, then drew in what sounded like a labored breath. "It's about Mike."

"THEY KILLED HIM, Vinny," Gina said. She and her brother, Vince, were sitting in the dark on her mother's glassed-in porch overlooking the snowy backyard. It had been several hours since Nick had called and, by now, probably half the people in Buffalo had heard the news from family and friends. But Gina was just beginning to make sense out of it.

"I never thought Mike was the kind to kill himself," her brother said.

"Me, either," she agreed. She hadn't. She'd never really believed that he would purposely abandon her and Emma. But the official ruling of suicide had caused her to question everything about her husband, her marriage. Her judgment.

"So, what happens now?" Vince asked.

"Well, Nick said there will be another trial. But, the guy has confessed. He's trying to bargain out of the death penalty. The killer was part of the same group of bad cops who tried to kill Nick. It seems that Mike had gotten involved with them, found out they were committing crimes, then decided to blow the whole thing open. They killed him and made it look like a suicide. Then T.J. found the tapes Mike made."

"How do you feel about that?"

"About the confession, about Mike's murder?" Gina sighed and looked through the dark glass of the windows toward the first flakes of new snow beginning to fall. "Relieved," she said, and drew in a breath of the cool air as the sadness inside her eased. Both she and Mike had been vindicated. "Now everyone knows what I've believed all along. Mike wasn't the bad guy."

She glanced sideways at her big brother. "Now maybe you can get off my case about whether or not I'm a good judge of character."

"Or not," her brother replied with a smirk.

Gina's thoughts went to Emma and how everything that had happened affected her. She'd been left without a father, but that didn't mean she couldn't grow and be assured of safety and love.

"What would you say if I told you I was thinking about quitting the police force?" she asked in a casual tone, just to see how Vince would react.

"You'd have my vote. I know you want to do something worthwhile, but I've never understood why you had to put your life on the line to do it."

Gina squirmed a little. "As tough as it is to admit this, I wanted to do something different from the rest of you, different from the safe, hometown family life. Mike understood that."

"I thought it had to do with something between you and Mike. But—"

"Mike's gone," Gina finished for him.

"Yeah. And you've got Emma."

"And now I envy what you have—the kids, the home, the marriage. I want Emma to know what that's like."

"Look, Sis, I know I've said this a hundred times but I wish you'd think about moving back here. You could live at Mom's, go back to school. Be a lawyer or a teacher, or anything you want. You could make a whole new start."

A whole new start. Unannounced, Jackson's face coalesced in Gina's thoughts. If she and Emma moved to Buffalo, they'd certainly never see him again. If they stayed in Atlanta . . . there was a chance. Slim, but a chance. And she had to see him, at least once more. She owed him an apology if nothing else.

"I'll think about it. I should warn you though, Emma asked me tonight when we were going home. She misses her friends and her new bike."

"You and I know she can make new friends. And if she lived here, she could have a sled. Maybe even a new dad."

Gina smiled again. "You never quit do you? You think there aren't any available men in Atlanta?"

Vinny shook his head. "If that biker is the best you can come up with, then you need to move, and fast."

"MOM, CAN I GO OUTSIDE and play in the snow?" Emma asked.

"That's *may* I. And, it's still snowing pretty hard. Why don't we wait until it slows down?" Gina answered. "Besides, you haven't finished your breakfast yet."

"I ate all my bacon."

"Finish your scrambled eggs and eat a half a piece of toast," Gina said as she put her own plate in the sink. She glanced out the kitchen window but she couldn't see much except the house next door. So she walked from the kitchen into the living room toward the front windows. Since she couldn't go out with Emma, she wanted to make sure there were other children in the park across the street on this snowy Saturday morning.

There were two, playing Frisbee with a dalmatian. Gina laughed as the dog jumped up on one of them and knocked him backward into the snow. Just as he scrambled back to his feet, a yellow cab pulled up in front of the house and claimed Gina's attention.

The windows of the cab were fogged giving no clue to the occupants. And it stopped at the driveway between her mother's house and the house next door.

"Mom? Are you expecting anyone?" Gina called.

"No, not that I know of." Her mother walked up behind her as Emma raced in from the kitchen.

As the three of them waited, the rear door of the cab opened and a man dressed in a heavy down coat got out. When he turned as if to read the number on the house, Gina's heartbeat seemed to rise to an insistent flutter in her chest.

"Mom!" Emma said. "It's Jackson!" She abandoned the window and ran for the door.

"Put on your coat!" Gina ordered, barely able to push the words out. "And be careful, the steps might be slippery." Then she turned and watched through the glass as her daughter raced down the driveway, heedless of the snow, toward the man Gina had thought she'd never see again.

"Who's this?" her mother asked, humor underlying her question.

"A friend," Gina answered without pulling her eyes away from Jackson.

"A friend of Emma's?" her mother persisted.

"No, Ma, mine..." Gina clarified. Then a terrible thought struck her. It wasn't fair. Jackson always caught her unprepared. With a self-conscious push at her hair she pivoted toward her mother. "Do I look all right?"

Her mother had the nerve to smile before patting her shoulder. "You look perfect."

WITH EMMA BALANCED on one hip and his duffel bag weighing down the other arm, Jackson made his way up the driveway. At least Emma was glad to see him. One down and about thirty to go. He felt like a green kid on his first night out about to face his date's parents. He didn't like the feeling. But he'd decided at the cabin that he'd face parents and brothers and whatever it took to find out if he and Gina could build something together.

"How's your mom?" he asked Emma.

"She's got a mooney boot to keep her cast out of the snow," Emma said as if that were the most important news to impart. "I got some, too. They're blue. Did you come to take us home tomorrow?"

"Well, that's up to your mom." Emma's innocent question brought more relief than Jackson wanted to admit to feeling. Gina wasn't staying in Buffalo long enough to find a job and a new life. At least not yet. "Is your Uncle Vince here?" he asked, dreading the answer.

"No. Only Grandma." Emma quickly lost interest in polite chitchat. "Will you build a snowman with me?"

"Yes, I will. But I have to say hello to your mom and meet your grandma first," he answered as he slowly went up the snowy stairs to the front door.

Jackson decided to knock rather than let Emma turn the handle and rush in. When the door opened, he gazed into the dark eyes of the one person he'd wanted to see for what seemed like years.

Gina . . .

"Jackson." Her voice sounded breathless and surprised. He couldn't tell if she was alarmed or excited.

His heart was pounding like a Led Zeppelin base track in high gear. He bent and allowed Emma to slide to the ground. She took his hand and towed him forward. But Gina was still blocking the doorway.

"Can I come in?" he asked.

"May Jackson come in, Mama?" Emma parroted.

Gina started as if she'd been jarred out of a trance. "Of course, come in." She moved back to give him room, then spoke to her daughter. "Emma, look at you. Your socks and shoes are soaking wet."

Emma checked out her soggy feet. "I forgot my moons," she confessed.

"Well, leave your coat and shoes here and go change your socks," Gina said as she held out a hand to help.

"I'll help her," Gina's mother said. "You take..." Her gaze shifted to Jackson in indecision.

"I'm sorry, Mom. This is Jackson. Jackson, this is my mother, Frances."

"Nice to meet you, ma'am," Jackson said as he set down his duffel and shrugged out of his coat.

"Very nice to meet you, too," Gina's mother said, sounding sincere. "Gina, you take Mr. Jackson's coat. I'll take Emma upstairs for new socks."

"But I want to talk to Jackson," Emma whined as her grandmother ushered her toward the stairs.

"In a while, in a while," Frances assured.

Standing alone in the hallway with Gina, the house suddenly seemed quieter and smaller. And Jackson experienced the terrible sinking sensation that he should have never come here. He was still the outsider, no matter how friendly Gina's mother had been in a pinch.

When Gina reached to take his coat he held on to it. "If you don't want me here, I can leave. Right now." He had to give her the out.

She met his gaze in surprise. As he watched, something in her expression warmed and softened. It was all he could do not to touch her.

"Don't be ridiculous," she said. She let go of his coat, then walked into his arms. "I'm really glad to see you," she said, her words muffled because her face was pressed into his shirt.

Jackson dropped the coat and tightened his arms around her. "Gina . . ." He couldn't think of a damned thing to say so he pushed his face into her hair and let his body speak for him. If she wanted him, he'd never let her go. Her family would have to pry them apart with power tools.

"I've got so much to tell you," she said.

"Me, too," he answered, but neither of them made an effort to go on.

When she finally pushed back to look up at him, there were tears sparkling in her eyes. But she laughed. "How in the world did you find us?"

Jackson stared down at her and all the words he'd rehearsed clogged in his throat. He'd forgotten how beautiful she was, how her smile made something go haywire in his chest. He used the fingers of his right hand to push a few strands of dark hair behind her ear before he answered her question. "Nick, the spy," he explained. Then he lowered his mouth to kiss her.

As Gina rose to meet his lips with her own, she felt suspended, fearless, like a kite, buoyed by a strong, familiar breeze. How had she survived for so long without kissing him?

The kiss, tentative at first, escalated into a slow, wet heat that warmed her whole body, part by part. She couldn't conceal a sigh when he ended it.

"Hi," he said, close to her mouth. "Remember me?"

Did she remember? She'd spent too many nights trying to forget. She kissed him lightly at the corner of his mouth. "It's beginning to come back to me. Are you going to tell me why you're here?"

He drew in a long breath as if he needed to prepare. "I decided I couldn't walk away and let it go—let you and Emma go. I'm here to fight."

"Fight?" Gina laughed.

"Mom?" Emma's voice came from the top of the stairs.

Jackson rolled his eyes at Emma's interruption, then he chuckled and slowly released her.

"What, Em?" Gina asked.

"Grandma wants to know if we can come back down now?"

Gina laughed at the idea that her mother had, by her actions, firmly declared herself an ally to this "friend" of hers—*Mr.* Jackson. What would Vince say to that? "Yes, you *may* come down now."

"I'M NOT SO SURE this is a good idea," Gina said as she stood on the steps staring at Jackson's broad back.

He arched a look backward over his shoulder. "Don't you trust me?" he asked and motioned with his hands for her to get closer.

"Come on, Mom!" Emma coaxed.

"Are you sure you're warm enough?" Gina checked her daughter over from head to toe, stalling for time. Then she had to laugh. Emma had so many clothes on she looked like a colorful mummy.

"Mooom!" Emma complained.

"Okay, okay," Gina placated, giving in. She moved closer to Jackson and put her hands on his shoulders. In one smooth motion, he dipped down and lifted her. Gina hadn't had a piggyback ride since she was six.

Jackson took a step forward and Gina tightened her arms around his neck. "Are you sure you can carry me?"

Jackson made a strangled sound of disgust. "Get real. You're hardly heavier than Emma. I think I can handle it." He made a wheezing sound. "You could loosen up on my throat a little, though."

They followed Emma down the driveway and across the street to the park. Jackson carried Gina to a bench, set her on her feet, then brushed the snow off for her to sit. He had his back to Emma which was his first mistake.

A snowball splattering against his rear end and a high-pitched giggle sent him into action.

Gina watched as he and Emma pelted each other with snow until they were both out of breath. The pristine blanket of white was crisscrossed with large and small footprints by the time Jackson called a truce. He walked over and sank down on the bench next to Gina.

"She has no respect for her elders," he said as he frowned and halfheartedly brushed at the melting snow in his hair.

"So, fight back," Gina suggested with an unsympathetic smirk. "You're bigger than she is."

Her words caused Jackson to gift her with one of his rare smiles and the impact held her immobile. Every argument she'd made for why they were all wrong for each other melted in the beauty of that smile. Gina knew without a doubt that she loved him. Now, what was she supposed to do about it?

"Jackson." Emma rushed over and pulled at one of his hands. "Let's build our snowman."

"Do you know how?" he asked.

"Sure," Emma answered. "You just make a big ball of snow." She raised her arms in a circle as large as her arms would stretch.

By the time the snowman had begun to take form, several other children had joined the project. When it looked as though Emma had all the help she needed, Jackson ducked out of the activity and joined Gina on the bench once more.

He sat down next to her and shoved back his jacket sleeve to see his watch. "Are you getting cold?" he asked. "We've been out here over an hour."

Dressed in one of the heavy jackets her mother kept in the closet for visitors, Gina was comfortable. "I'm fine." She didn't want to go inside yet. Now that Emma was occupied, Gina wanted to use the opportunity to talk to Jackson.

"Jackson, I want to apologize for the way my brother treated you that night at T.J.'s." She held his gaze. "I've been sick about it."

He looked away, toward the busy builders. "Yeah, well. I guess I have to stop being so sensitive about my life and how other people see it. And I suppose he meant well, trying to protect you—"

"No, he didn't." Gina's reply brought Jackson's surprised gaze back to hers. "He was guarding his territory, and testing you. He knows I wouldn't allow any man into my life who might hurt Emma. I'm a cop, and a mother. I know the signs."

Gina looked down at her hands. "I'm also sorry I didn't defend you a little better. It won't happen again."

Jackson stared at her for several long seconds, before asking, "What does 'allow into your life' mean?" Then he seemed to think better of asking and stopped her before she could reply. "Listen, I know I'm not like Mike, and I couldn't be a father to my own child, but I came up here to ask you if you'd let me look after you and Emma. We could all take care of each other."

"No, you're not like Mike," Gina agreed. "But you're here. And, I've decided I like having you around."

"Like?"

She couldn't break away from his expectant gaze. "Yeah, a lot," she said slowly hoping he could see the truth in her eyes. "More than I realized I would on New Year's Eve. And I've been doing some thinking about that white picket fence thing. I've decided that it's a state of mind not an actual place."

"You think?" Jackson asked.

"Yeah, it's more like a quality of life rather than where you live." She looked out over the snowy park. "It's like watching you build a snowman with Emma. That's real life." She gazed at him once more. "You're quality, Jackson, under that bad-boy face you wear for the world."

His smile warmed her all over again like a brush with the sun. "Then Uncle Vince will have a hard time getting rid of me."

As Jackson leaned closer to kiss her, Emma slogged over to them out of breath and collapsed at their feet. "Come and see, we gave him eyes and a mouth," she said pointing to the snowman.

"That's great," Gina replied, without taking her gaze from Jackson.

"Mooom, look," Emma persisted.

Gina gazed at her daughter instead, unwilling to succumb to whining. Emma's nose and cheeks were as red as a strawberry and her hands were bare. "Where are your gloves?" she asked. Without giving her time to answer, she said, "Go get them. I think we need to go inside and warm up for a while."

"But Mom—"

"I bet Grandma has some hot chocolate ready for you," Gina added. "Let's go, Em. You can come back out later."

Without further argument, Emma went to retrieve her gloves. Jackson helped Gina stand then bent his knees and pulled her onto his back again.

"This piggyback thing is sort of kinky," Jackson said as he drew her thighs higher and tighter around him. "I like it."

"You *are* weird," Gina said laughing, then nipped his ear with her teeth.

"Love does that to a man."

Gina went still for a moment. "Love?"

"Sure. You know, that promise between a man and a woman. Forever after. Love."

She tightened her hold around his neck and planted a kiss behind his ear. "Yeah," she whispered. "I know."

They walked past several cars parked on the street then the last ten feet of the driveway became a footrace between Emma and Jackson with Gina along as an unwilling passenger. Emma won and they were all laughing and out of breath by the time they reached the stairs to the front door.

Before Emma could turn the knob, the door opened. Vince stood on the threshold.

"What are you doing here?" he asked, his unfriendly gaze on Jackson.

Jackson started to lower Gina to the ground, but she held on, sending a silent and not so subtle message to her brother.

Emma answered the question. "Jackson came to take us home."

Epilogue

"EVERYTHING'S PERFECT!" Tyler exclaimed. He gazed out over the elegant courtyard filled with spring flowers and wedding guests like a feudal lord surveying his domain. "I knew it wouldn't rain today." Then, his attention shifted. He looked at his watch. "Where's the groom?"

Jackson had dodged Tyler for most of the morning but he knew it was time to give up and follow orders. "Right here," he said although he was sure Tyler could see him perfectly, standing a few feet away with Nick and Gina's brother Vince. "And, I have the flowers." He raised the bridal bouquet that he'd been assigned to hold for safekeeping.

"You look good in a tux . . . and flowers," Nick said with a smirk.

"Well, I thought I would never live to see it," Tyler added with a dramatic roll of his eyes.

Jackson let it slide. Nothing could ruin this day for him. He was getting what he wanted—Gina, and Emma. Nothing else mattered. "You've done a great job, Tyler. As usual," he said.

Tyler didn't look completely convinced. "At least the weather is cooperating." He turned to Jackson with a frown. "You nearly gave me a heart attack when you started building that fence, but I've sort of gotten used to it now. Heaven knows what the owners of the complex will say when they see it."

"Is that what you call New Age, industrial art?" Vince asked. "Whoever heard of a picket fence attached to a wall? And made of metal?" He stared at the smooth steel slats connected into a stylized fence that crossed the entire facade of Jackson's studio like a jagged line of lightning.

Jackson merely smiled. "Tyler wouldn't let me put it in the courtyard," he said. He gave Vince a meaningful stare. "Different strokes for different folks. Gina likes it."

"Yes, and the value of the complex went up," Tyler added. "The owners will appreciate that. Now, let's get going. It's time. Jackson, give Vince the flowers," he ordered. "You and I and Nick need to go up front."

"Hey," Vince said as he accepted the bouquet from his soon to be brother-in-law. He stared into Jackson's eyes as if they were the only two men in the courtyard. "You take care of my sister and Em, understand?"

Jackson didn't smile although he knew he'd just heard the closest thing he was likely to get as a welcome to the family from Vince. "Yeah, I understand," he answered and walked away toward the ten-foot arch of flowers that Tyler had constructed at the far end of the court-yard. And toward his new future.

Emma's friend Courtney came down the walkway first, then her mother, Vickie. Next came Emma dressed in pale blue with most of the ribbons still left in her hair and tossing rose petals like a fairy princess sprinkling magic dust. He winked at her when she reached the front and she grinned before scooting next to Court-ney.

Then Jackson's eyes were on Gina as Vince escorted her down the aisle. She was wearing blue also, but not the kind of blues she'd been wearing on New Year's Eve. Whoever could have foreseen Jackson Gray, marrying a police officer and becoming a dad all in one day? He was sure his own father would be rolling on the ground laughing if he were here to see it. But this was right. Everything had come around full circle and now the circle was filled with love.

Then suddenly Gina was gazing up at him and say-ing the vows. And when it was his turn, and he got to "until death do us part," he smiled and added, "forever after."

* * *

It Happened One Night continues next month, with CHANGE OF HEART by *Janice Kaiser*.

This month's
irresistible novels from

NEW YEAR'S KNIGHT by Lyn Ellis

It Happened One Night...

Everyone was celebrating—except Gina Tarantino. Ringing in the New Year only made her realize how alone she was. Then at the stroke of midnight, her luck changed with a passionate embrace from a magnificent male... A sizzling night with Jackson Gray started the year *exactly* as she meant it to go on!

A NIGHT TO REMEMBER by Gina Wilkins

Andrew Colton Tyler had everything money could buy...but his life was too predictable. Then on New Year's Eve, Nicky Holiday turned his world upside down. After one night of living and loving that he'd *never* forget, there was no going back: he *had* to keep her once the adventure was over!

THE TROUBLE WITH TONYA by Lorna Michaels

Tonya's life was a mess but why on earth had her grandfather found her work at a youth centre? She knew nothing about kids! Then she met Kirk Butler, the centre's hunky director, and sent his pulse rate soaring. But that was just the beginning—Kirk had no idea just *how* much trouble Tonya could be...

TWICE THE SPICE by Patricia Ryan

Double Dare

Emma Sutclifffe was content playing the 'good' twin to her outrageous double, Zara. But there was no going back after she walked a mile in Zara's killer spike heels—followed by the sexiest man she'd *ever* seen. And it looked like she would have Gage Foster on her heels until she gave him exactly what he wanted...

Spoil yourself next month
with these four novels from

CHANGE OF HEART by Janice Kaiser

It Happened One Night...

'Twas the night before Valentine's Day...and Liz Cabot was out
celebrating her engagement with her girlfriends. She didn't
expect to run into her first love, Colby Sommers. Or spend the
night making mad passionate love with this heartbreaker. When
she woke up the next day, who would be her valentine?

MR VALENTINE by Vicki Lewis Thompson

Jack Killigan's book had just been published but there was one
hitch—his publisher thought he was a woman! After all, his
novel *was* a hot, steamy romance! So Jack persuaded his
childhood friend Krysta Lueckenhoff to fill in for him. Soon
she's intrigued—can her old friend make love as well as he
writes it?

THE GETAWAY BRIDE by Gina Wilkins

Brides on the Run

Gabe Conroy had been the happiest man in the world—until he'd
returned home to find his new bride had disappeared.
Devastated, he vowed he would never stop looking for her. But,
once he found his runaway wife, what was he going to do with
her?

RESTLESS NIGHTS by Tiffany White

Blaze

Victoria Stone had had plenty of erotic fantasies, but until she met
Zack DeLuca she never imagined experiencing them for real. Not
in her wildest dreams had Victoria pictured herself responding so
brazenly to a perfect stranger. And it was completely crazy to go
away on holiday with him...where things could only get hotter...

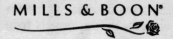

MILLS & BOON®

*Especially for
you on*
Mother's Day

Four fabulous new heart-warming romances
inside one attractive gift pack.

JUST FOR A NIGHT - Miranda Lee

A MAN WORTH WAITING FOR - Helen Brooks

TO DR CARTWRIGHT, A DAUGHTER
- Meredith Webber

BABY SWAP - Suzanne Carey

**Special Offer—1 book FREE!
Retail price only £6.60**

On sale February 1998

4 FREE
books and a surprise gift!

We would like to take this opportunity to thank you for reading this Mills & Boon® book by offering you the chance to take FOUR more specially selected titles from the Temptation® series absolutely FREE! We're also making this offer to introduce you to the benefits of the Reader Service™—

- ★ FREE home delivery
- ★ FREE gifts and competitions
- ★ FREE monthly newsletter
- ★ Books available before they're in the shops
- ★ Exclusive Reader Service discounts

Accepting these FREE books and gift places you under no obligation to buy, you may cancel at any time, even after receiving your free shipment. Simply complete your details below and return the entire page to the address below. *You don't even need a stamp!*

YES! Please send me 4 free Temptation books and a surprise gift. I understand that unless you hear from me, I will receive 4 superb new titles every month for just £2.20 each, postage and packing free. I am under no obligation to purchase any books and may cancel my subscription at any time. The free books and gift will be mine to keep in any case.

T8XE

Ms/Mrs/Miss/Mr ....Initials ....
BLOCK CAPITALS PLEASE

Surname ....

Address ....

....

....Postcode....................................

Send this whole page to:
THE READER SERVICE, FREEPOST, CROYDON, CR9 3WZ
(Eire readers please send coupon to: P.O. BOX 4546, DUBLIN 24.)